Lecture Notes in Mathematics

A collection of informal reports and seminars
Edited by A. Dold, Heidelberg and B. Eckmann, Zürich

140

J. Glimm, L. Gross, Harish-Chandra,
R. V. Kadison, D. Ruelle, I. E. Segal

Lectures in Modern Analysis and Applications II

Edited by C. T. Taam, George Washington University

Springer-Verlag
Berlin · Heidelberg · New York 1970

PREFACE

This lecture series in Modern Analysis and Applications was sponsored by the Consortium of Universities (American University, Catholic University, Georgetown University, George Washington University, and Howard University) in Washington, D.C. and the University of Maryland, in conjunction with the U.S. Air Force Office of Scientific Research. These lectures were presented at the sponsoring universities over the period 1967-69 by mathematicians who have contributed much to the recent growth of analysis.

The series consisted of eight (8) sessions of three lectures each. Each session was devoted to an active basic area of contemporary analysis which is important in application or shows potential applications. Each lecture presented a survey and a critical review of certain aspects of that area, with emphasis on new result, open problem, and application.

The eight sessions of the series were devoted to the following basic areas of analysis:

1. Modern Methods and New Results in Complex Analysis
2. Banach Algebras and Applications
3. Topological Linear Spaces and Applications
4. Geometric and Qualitative Aspects of Analysis
5. Analysis and Representation Theory
6. Modern Analysis and New Physical Theories
7. Modern Harmonic Analysis and Applications
8. Integration in Function Spaces and Applications.

This volume contains six lectures from the fifth, sixth and eighth sessions. Some of the manuscripts were proof-read by the editor after they were retyped for reproduction, the editor would be grateful to have the authors' understanding in this matter which was due to the pressures of time.

C. T. Taam

George Washington University

ORGANIZING COMMITTEE

George H. Butcher
Howard University

Avron Douglis
University of Maryland

John E. Lagnese
Georgetown University

Raymond W. Moller
Catholic University of America

Robert G. Pohrer
U.S. Air Force Office of Scientific Research

Steven H. Schot
American University

C. T. Taam, Chairman
George Washington University

Elmer West
Consortium of Universities

TABLE OF CONTENTS

Professor DAVID RUELLE, Institut des Hautes Études Scientifique

New Methods and Problems in Statistical Mechanics....................68

Recent developments in the statistical mechanics of infinite systems will be discussed. Some insight into the meaning of the Gibbs phase rule is obtained.

INTEGRATION IN FUNCTION SPACES AND APPLICATIONS

Professor LEONARD GROSS, Cornell University

Abstract Wiener Measure and Infinite Dimensional Potential Theory....84

Basic definitions and concepts in the theory of integration over infinite dimensional vector spaces will be described. Newtonian potential theory on Euclidean n-space will be extended to potential theory on an infinite dimensional Hilbert space as an application and motivation. It will be shown how Wiener space arises from these considerations.

Contents of Lectures in Modern Analysis and Applications I..........117

Some applications of the Schwartz space of a semisimple Lie group

by Harish-Chandra

Let G be a connected semisimple Lie group with finite center. Then in a paper in Acta [1(a)], I have introduced a space $\mathscr{C}(G)$ of functions on G, which I call the Schwartz space of G. I shall not define it here but recall some of its properties.

1) $C_c^\infty(G) \subset \mathscr{C}(G) \subset C^\infty(G)$. $\mathscr{C}(G)$ is a complete, locally convex Hausdorff space and $C_c^\infty(G)$ is dense in $\mathscr{C}(G)$. Moreover the inclusion mapping of $C_c^\infty(G)$ into $\mathscr{C}(G)$ is continuous.

2) Let $\mathfrak{g}$ be the Lie algebra of G. Then for any $X \in \mathfrak{g}$, the corresponding left- and right-invariant vector-fields L_X and R_X, define continuous endomorphisms of $\mathscr{C}(G)$. $\mathscr{C}(G)$ is stable under left and right translations of G and the corresponding representations of G on $\mathscr{C}(G)$ are continuous.

3) $\mathscr{C}(G) \subset L_2(G)$.

4) $\mathscr{C}(G)$ is closed under convolution.[1)]

5) "Wave-packets" lie in $\mathscr{C}(G)$. (This property, which is crucial, is more precisely expressed in Theorem 6.)

Let u be a differential operator on G. Its adjoint u^* is the differential operator given by the relation

$$\int_G uf.\,g dx = \int_G f.\,u^* g dx \qquad (f, g \in C_c^\infty(G)),$$

where dx is the Haar measure of G. Let T be a distribution on G. Then the mapping $f \longrightarrow T(u^* f)$ $(f \in C_c^\infty(G))$ is also a distribution which we denote by uT. As usual we identify a locally summable function F on G with the distribution T_F given by

$$T_F(f) = \int F f dx \qquad (f \in C_c^\infty(G)).$$

Fix a maximal compact subgroup K of G and let $\mathfrak{Z}$ denote the algebra of all differential operators on G which commute with both left and right translations of G. A distribution T on G is said to be $\mathfrak{Z}$-finite if the space of all distributions of the form zT $(z \in \mathfrak{Z})$ has finite dimension. Similarly it is called K-finite if the left and right translates of T under K, span a vector-space of finite dimension

Theorem 1. Any K-finite and $\mathfrak{Z}$-finite function in $L_2(G)$ lies in $\mathcal{C}(G)$.

This shows that $\mathcal{C}(G)$ contains the "wave-packet" corresponding to a point in the discrete spectrum.

By a parabolic subgroup (psgp) P of G, we mean a closed subgroup of G with the following two properties.

1) If $\mathfrak{p}$ is the Lie algebra of P, then $\mathfrak{p}_c$ contains a Borel subalgebra (i.e. a maximal solvable subalgebra) of $\mathfrak{g}_c$.

2) P is the normalizer of $\mathfrak{p}$ in G.

By the radical N of P, we mean the maximal normal subgroup of P such that Ad(n) is unipotent for every $n \in N$. For any $f \in \mathcal{C}(G)$, put

$$f^P(x) = \int_N f(xn)dn \qquad (x \in G) ,$$

where dn is the Haar measure on N. (This integral always exists.) We say that f is a cusp form if $f^P = 0$ for every psgp $P \neq G$. Let ${}^0\mathcal{C}(G)$ denote the space of all cusp forms on G. Then ${}^0\mathcal{C}(G)$ is a closed subspace of $\mathcal{C}(G)$.

Theorem 2. Every $\mathfrak{Z}$-finite function in $\mathcal{C}(G)$ is a cusp form. Conversely $\mathfrak{Z}$-finite functions are dense in ${}^0\mathcal{C}(G)$.

Put $\mathcal{H} = L_2(G)$ and let ${}^0\mathcal{H}$ denote the closure of ${}^0\mathcal{C}(G)$ in $\mathcal{H}$. Let λ denote the left-regular representation of G on $\mathcal{H}$.

Theorem 3. ${}^0\mathcal{H}$ is an orthogonal sum of invariant and irreducible subspaces. Conversely every irreducible subspace of $\mathcal{H}$ is contained in ${}^0\mathcal{H}$. Let ${}^0E$ denote the orthogonal projection of $\mathcal{H}$ on ${}^0\mathcal{H}$. Then ${}^0E\,\mathcal{C}(G) = {}^0\mathcal{C}(G)$ and

^{o}E defines a continuous mapping of $\mathcal{C}(G)$ onto $^{o}\mathcal{C}(G)$.

Theorem 4. $^{o}\mathcal{C}(G) \neq \{0\}$ if and only if rank G = rank K.

Let τ be a unitary double representation of K on a finite-dimensional Hilbert space V. Let $\mathcal{C}(G, \tau)$ denote the set of all $f \in \mathcal{C}(G) \otimes V$ such that $f(k_1 x k_2) = \tau(k_1)f(x)\tau(k_2)$ $(k_1, k_2 \in K,\ x \in G)$. We denote by $^{o}\mathcal{C}(G,\tau)$ the space of all cusp forms in $\mathcal{C}(G, \tau)$.

Lemma 1. $\dim {}^{o}\mathcal{C}(G, \tau) < \infty$.

Let θ denote the Cartan involution of G with respect to K. An abelian subgroup A of G is said to split, if for every $a \in A$, Ad(a) can be diagonalized over $\mathbb{R}$. Let P be a psgp and N its radical. Put $M_1 = P \cap \theta(P)$ and let A be a maximal connected split abelian subgroup lying in the center of M_1. Then A is unique and M_1 is the centralizer of A in G. Let $X(M_1)$ denote the group of all continuous homomorphisms of M_1 into the multiplicative group $\mathbb{R}^{\times}$ of real numbers. Put

$$M = \bigcap_{\chi \in X(M_1)} \ker |\chi|$$

where $|\chi|(m) = |\chi(m)|$ $(\chi \in X(M_1),\ m \in M_1)$. Then $M_1 = MA$, $P = MAN$ and the corresponding mapping of $M \times A \times N$ into P is a diffeomorphism. We call this the Langlands decomposition of P, and A the split component of P. Let $\mathfrak{a}$ be the Lie algebra of A. Then the exponential mapping defines a bijection of $\mathfrak{a}$ on A. M is a reductive group with finitely many connected components and $K_M = K \cap M$ is a maximal compact subgroup of M. Let τ_M denote the restriction of τ on K_M. Then the spaces $\mathcal{C}(M)$, $^{o}\mathcal{C}(M)$ and $^{o}\mathcal{C}(M, \tau_M)$ can be defined in the same way as above.

Let $\mathfrak{h}$ be a Cartan subalgebra of $\mathfrak{g}$. By $\mathfrak{h}_R$ we mean the set of all points in $\mathfrak{h}$ where every root of $(\mathfrak{g}, \mathfrak{h})$ takes a real value.
A psgp P = MAN is called cuspidal if $^{o}\mathcal{C}(M) \neq \{0\}$.

Lemma 2. P is cuspidal if and only if there exists a θ-stable Cartan subalgebra $\mathfrak{h}$ of $\mathfrak{g}$ such that $\mathfrak{a} = \mathfrak{h}_R$.

Let $f \in \mathcal{C}(G)$ and $P = MAN$ a psgp of G. We write $f^P \sim 0$ if[2)]

$$\int_M \operatorname{conj} \phi(m) . f^P(xm)dm = 0$$

for all $x \in G$ and $\phi \in {}^{\circ}\mathcal{C}(M)$. Here dm is the Haar measure on M and the integral always exists.

Lemma 3. Let f be an element in $\mathcal{C}(G)$ such that $f^P \sim 0$ for all cuspidal subgroups P of G. Then $f = 0$.

This is the analogue of a theorem of Langlands [1(b), Theorem 4, p. 16].

Two psgps P_1, P_2 are said to be associated, if their split components A_1, A_2 are conjugate under G (or equivalently under K).

Let $\mathfrak{h}_i = \theta(\mathfrak{h}_i)$ $(1 \leq i \leq r)$ be a complete set of Cartan subalgebras, no two of which are conjugate under G. Put $\mathfrak{a}_i = \mathfrak{h}_{i,R}$ and $A_i = \exp \mathfrak{a}_i$. Let $\mathcal{C}_i(G)$ denote the set of all $f \in \mathcal{C}(G)$ with the following property. If $P = MAN$ is any cuspidal subgroup of G, then $f^P \sim 0$ unless A is conjugate to A_i under K. Then $\mathcal{C}_i(G)$ is a closed subspace of $\mathcal{C}(G)$.

Theorem 5. $\mathcal{C}(G) = \sum_{1 \leq i \leq r} \mathcal{C}_i(G)$ where the sum is direct and smooth.

Let E_i denote the projection of $\mathcal{C}(G)$ on $\mathcal{C}_i(G)$ corresponding to the above direct sum. Then smoothness means that E_i are continuous endomorphisms of $\mathcal{C}(G)$. This theorem and its proof are closely related to the Plancherel formula for G.

Let $P = MAN$ be a psgp of G. Then $G = KP$ and therefore any $x \in G$ can be written as $x = kman$ $(k \in K,\ m \in M,\ a \in A,\ n \in N)$. The element a being unique, we define $H_P(x) = \log a \in \mathfrak{a}$. Also put

$$\rho_P(H) = \frac{1}{2} \operatorname{tr}(\operatorname{ad} H)_{\mathfrak{n}} \qquad (H \in \mathfrak{a}) ,$$

$\mathfrak{n}$ being the Lie algebra of N.

Now suppose P is cuspidal. Then from Lemma 1, $L = {}^{\circ}\mathcal{C}(M, \tau_M)$ is a finite-dimensional space. Given $\phi \in L$, we extend it to a function on G as follows:

$$\phi(kman) = \tau(k)\phi(m) \qquad (k \in K,\ m \in M,\ a \in A,\ n \in N) .$$

Let $\mathfrak{a}^*$ denote the space dual to $\mathfrak{a}$. For any $\Lambda \in \mathfrak{a}_c^*$ and $\phi \in L$, define

$$E(P : \phi : \Lambda : x) = \int_K \phi(xk)\tau(k^{-1})\exp\{((-1)^{1/2}\Lambda - \rho_P)(H_P(xk))\}dk \qquad (x \in G) ,$$

where dk is the normalized Haar measure on K. Then for fixed ϕ and x, this is an entire function of $\Lambda \in \mathfrak{a}_c^*$. Let $\mathfrak{Z}_M$ be the analogue of $\mathfrak{Z}$ for M. If ϕ is an eigenfunction of $\mathfrak{Z}_M$, then $E(P : \phi : \Lambda)$ is an eigenfunction of $\mathfrak{Z}$. We call $E(P : \phi : \Lambda)$ the Eisenstein integral in analogy with the Eisenstein series (see [1(b), p. 29] and [2(a), (b)]).

Let $d\Lambda$ denote the Euclidean measure on $\mathfrak{a}^*$ and $\mathscr{C}(\mathfrak{a}^*)$ the usual Schwartz space for $\mathfrak{a}^*$.

Theorem 6. There exists a polynomial function $q \neq 0$ on $\mathfrak{a}^*$, with the following property. For any $f \in \mathscr{C}(\mathfrak{a}^*) \otimes L$, the integral

$$E(P : f : x) = \int_{\mathfrak{a}^*} q(\Lambda)E(P : f(\Lambda) : \Lambda : x)d\Lambda \qquad (x \in G)$$

converges, $E(P : f) \in \mathscr{C}(G,\tau)$ and

$$f \longrightarrow E(P : f)$$

is a continuous mapping of $\mathscr{C}(\mathfrak{a}^*) \otimes L$ into $\mathscr{C}(G,\tau)$.

Roughly speaking, this theorem says that wave-packets lie in $\mathscr{C}(G)$.

Lemma 4. Let P' be another psgp of G. Then if $f \in \mathscr{C}(\mathfrak{a}^*) \otimes L$,

$$E(P : f)^{P'} \sim 0$$

unless P and P' are associated.

Fix i $(1 \leq i \leq r)$ such that A is conjugate to A_i under K. (Since P is cuspidal there exists a unique such index i.) Put $\mathscr{C}_i(G,\tau) = \mathscr{C}(G,\tau) \cap (\mathscr{C}_i(G) \otimes V)$. Then Lemma 4 shows that

$E(P : f) \in \mathcal{C}_i(G, \tau)$.

Let $P = MAN$ as above. By a root of (P, A) we mean an element $\alpha \in \mathfrak{a}^*$ such that $[H, X] = \alpha(H)X$ for all $H \in \mathfrak{a}$ and some $X \neq 0$ in $\mathfrak{n}$. Fix a norm on $\mathfrak{a}$ and let a be a variable element in A. We say that $a \xrightarrow[P]{} \infty$ if $|\log a| \longrightarrow \infty$ and there exists a number $\varepsilon > 0$ such that $\alpha(\log a) \geq \varepsilon |\log a|$ for every root α of (P, A). Put

$$w = w(A) = (\text{Normalizer of } A \text{ in } G)/(\text{Centralizer of } A \text{ in } G) .$$

Then w operates on $\mathfrak{a}$ and $\mathfrak{a}^*$ in the usual way.

Let $P = MAN$, $P' = MAN'$ be two psgps with the same split component A. Then if $\Lambda \in \mathfrak{a}^*$ is not too special (i.e. does not lie on a certain finite set of hyperplanes passing through the origin), there exist unique endomorphisms $c_{P'|P}(s : \Lambda)$ $(s \in w)$ of L such that

$$\lim_{a \xrightarrow[P']{} \infty} \left| e^{\rho'(\log a)} E(P : \phi : \Lambda : ma) - \sum_{s \in w} (c_{P'|P}(s : \Lambda)\phi)(m) e^{(-1)^{1/2} s\Lambda(\log a)} \right| = 0$$

for all $m \in M$ and $\phi \in L$. (Here $\rho' = \rho_{P'}$.) Regarded as functions of Λ, $c_{P'|P}(s : \Lambda)$ are meromorphic on $\mathfrak{a}^* + (-1)^{1/2} U$ where U is an open neighborhood of zero in $\mathfrak{a}^*$. But it seems likely that they are actually meromorphic in the whole complex space $\mathfrak{a}_c^*$. Moreover $\det c_{P|P}(1 : \Lambda)$ is not identically zero[3] in Λ. Put

$$E^o(P : \phi : \Lambda) = E(P : c_{P|P}(1 : \Lambda)^{-1}\phi : \Lambda) .$$

Then I believe the following statements are true although the full proofs have not yet been worked out.

1) $E^o(P : \phi : \Lambda)$ is a meromorphic function of $\Lambda \in \mathfrak{a}_c^*$ which is holomorphic on $\mathfrak{a}^*$.

2) It satisfies functional equations very similar to those known for the Eisenstein series (see [1(b), p. 114] and [2(a), (b)]).

Finally, I am inclined to believe that entirely analogous results hold for the corresponding Eisenstein integrals in the $\mathfrak{p}$-adic case as well. But this is, at present, a largely unexplored territory.

The Institute for Advanced Study
Princeton, N. J.

References

1. Harish-Chandra, (a) "Discrete series for semisimple Lie groups II," Acta Math., vol. 116 (1966), pp. 1-111.
(b) "Automorphic forms on semisimple Lie groups," Notes by J. G. M. Mars, Lecture Notes in Mathematics, vol. 62 (1968), Springer-Verlag.

2. R. P. Langlands, (a) "On the functional equations satisfied by Eisenstein Series," Mimeographed manuscript, 1965 (unpublished).
(b) "Eisenstein Series," Algebraic groups and discontinuous groups (1966), Amer. Math. Soc., pp. 235-252.

Footnotes

[1] In case of $SL(2,\mathbb{R})$, this fact had been observed by Langlands.

[2] conj c denotes the conjugate of a complex number c.

[3] This was pointed out to me by Langlands.

SOME ANALYTIC METHODS IN THE THEORY OF OPERATOR ALGEBRAS

by Richard V. Kadison*

1. INTRODUCTION

Our aim, in this article, is to illustrate the application of some analytic techniques, drawn from the mathematical theory of quantized fields, to the study of (one-parameter) groups of automorphisms of C*-algebras. These illustrations take the form of three theorems stated and proved in §3, §4 and §5.

Stronger results than the three theorems presented are valid. They apply to many (rather than, one) - parameter groups; and are obtained by applying methods from the theory of several complex variables where we have used those of the theory of functions of one complex variable. The choice of the simpler theorems is prompted by easy accessibility and clarity of method.

These theorems result from adapting more complicated statements arising in the mathematical treatment of certain physical disciplines to simpler circumstances. The physical assumption of 'positive energy' is at the heart of the analytic techniques by which they are proved. The section which follows recalls some basic results and draws the analytic consequence of the positive energy assumption used in their proofs.

---

*Completed with partial support from NSF. This article is an expanded version of a lecture delivered October 5, 1968 to The Consortium of Universities at George Washington University in Washington, D.C.

2. PRELIMINARY RESULTS

The Hilbert spaces with which we deal are over the field $\mathbb{C}$ of complex scalars. We denote by '$\mathbb{C}_+$' and '$\mathbb{C}_-$' the (closed) upper and lower half-planes in $\mathbb{C}$, respectively ($\{z : \text{Im } z \geq 0\}$ and $\{z : \text{Im } z \leq 0\}$); and by '$\overset{\circ}{\mathbb{C}}_+$' and '$\overset{\circ}{\mathbb{C}}_-$' the corresponding open half-planes. We denote the inner product of two vectors ϕ and ψ, in a Hilbert space $\mathcal{H}$ by '(ϕ,ψ)' and the bound and adjoint of a bounded operator A on $\mathcal{H}$ by '$\|A\|$' and 'A^*', respectively.

A family $\mathfrak{U}$ of bounded operators on $\mathcal{H}$ which contains AB, $aA + B$ and A^* when it contains A and B and which is closed with respect to the metric (norm) topology induced by $A \to \|A\|$, on the family, $\mathcal{B}(\mathcal{H})$, of all bounded operators on $\mathcal{H}$ is called 'a C^*-algebra'. Those C^*-algebras, $\mathcal{R}$, closed with respect to the strong (operator) topology on $\mathcal{B}(\mathcal{H})$ (the topology of convergence on vectors of $\mathcal{H}$) are called 'von Neumann algebras'.

Denoting by $\mathcal{F}'$ the set of operators in $\mathcal{B}(\mathcal{H})$ commuting with every operator in $\mathcal{F}(\subseteq \mathcal{B}(\mathcal{H}))$ ($\mathcal{F}'$ is called 'the commutant' of $\mathcal{F}$), von Neumann proves, in [9] , his:

Double Commutant Theorem. _If $\mathcal{R}$ is a von Neumann algebra containing the identity operator I then_ $(\mathcal{R}')' = \mathcal{R}$.

The set, $\mathcal{U}(\mathcal{H})$, of unitary operators on $\mathcal{H}$ together with the strong operator topology induced on it from that on $\mathcal{B}(\mathcal{H})$ is a topological group. A continuous homomorphism of another topological group G into the topological group $\mathcal{U}(\mathcal{H})$ is called ' a strongly continuous unitary representation of G on $\mathcal{H}$'. Stone's Theorem [14] classifies all such representations of the additive group, $\mathbb{R}$, of real numbers (with its usual metric topology). If $t \to U_t$ is such a representation (called 'a strongly continuous one-parameter unitary group') on $\mathcal{H}$, this theorem asserts the existence of a (not necessarily bounded) self-adjoint operator H on $\mathcal{H}$ such that $U_t = \exp(-itH)$, for each real t, where $\exp(-itH)$ is understood in the sense of the functional calculus associated with the spectral resolution of H.

We shall have occasion to use this functional calculus in its strong form. The self-adjoint operators are represented as the operations of multiplication by bounded measurable functions on the $\mathcal{L}_2$-space of some measure space, in this version. The process of forming a function of an operator becomes that of composing the function with the 'multiplier' function corresponding to the operator to arrive at the 'multiplier' function corresponding to the desired function of the operator. In more detail, it is proved that if $\mathcal{A}$ is a maximal abelian von Neumann algebra on $\mathcal{H}$, then there are a measure space X, a regular Borel measure m on X and a unitary transformation U of $\mathcal{H}$ onto $\mathcal{L}_2(X)$ such that $U\mathcal{A}U^{-1} = \mathfrak{M}$, with $\mathfrak{M} = \{M_f : f$ a bounded m-measurable function on $X\}$ and M_f is the (bounded) operator defined on $\mathcal{L}_2(X)$ by: $M_f(g) = f \cdot g$. The unbounded self-adjoint operators whose spectral projections lie in $\mathcal{A}$ are transformed by U onto multiplications by unbounded m-measurable functions. If h is, say, continuous on $\mathbb{R}$ and A is in $\mathcal{A}$, then $U\,h(A)U^{-1} = M_{h \circ f}$, where $UAU^{-1} = M_f$ (cf. [12; Theorem 1, p. 5]).

In its usual form, the observables of a quantum mechanical system are associated with the self-adjoint operators on $\mathcal{H}$. The physical states of the system are associated with the unit vectors in $\mathcal{H}$ (up to a complex multiple of modulus 1). The time development of the system, for a specified set of dynamics, is given by a (strongly continuous) one-parameter unitary group $t \to U_t$ (= exp-itH). The system, in a state corresponding to the unit vector ψ, will evolve, after time t, into the state corresponding to $U_t\psi$ (in a Schrödinger Picture of dynamics). The Hamiltonian H of the system corresponds to the total energy of the system (up to a constant multiple)--its spectral values being the various possible energy levels. The 'positive energy' assumption, we shall make in the statements of the theorems of the succeeding sections takes the form: $H \geq 0$. (For these results, it would do as well to assume that H is bounded below or above--that is, semi-bounded.)

The automorphisms α of the C^*-algebra $\mathfrak{A}$ with which we deal are assumed to preserve the adjoint structure as well as the algebraic structure of $\mathfrak{A}$ (i.e. $\alpha(A^*) = \alpha(A)^*$). With $t \to U_t$ specifying the time development of a physical system whose (bounded) observables are identified with the self-adjoint operators in $\mathfrak{A}$, the assumption we will make, that $(\alpha_t(A) =)\ U_tAU_{-t} \in \mathfrak{A}$ for each real t and each A in $\mathfrak{A}$, is equivalent to assuming that the mappings α_t are automorphisms of $\mathfrak{A}$. It is also the case that $t \to \alpha_t$ is a one-parameter group of automorphisms of $\mathfrak{A}$ (a homomorphism of $\mathbb{R}$ into the group of automorphisms of $\mathfrak{A}$). These automorphisms specify the time-development of the system in a 'Heisenberg Picture' of the dynamics. An observable corresponding to A evolves, after time t, into the observable corresponding to $\alpha_t(A)$. We shall be especially interested in those automorphisms α of $\mathfrak{A}$ such that there is a unitary operater U in $\mathcal{U}$ for which $\alpha(A) = UAU^{-1}$ for all A in $\mathcal{U}$. Such α are said to be <u>inner</u>.

With the assumption that $H \geq 0$, $t \to U_t$ (=exp-itH) can be extended to the lower half-plane $\mathbb{C}_-$ with certain continuity and analyticity conditions holding. Define U_z to be exp(-izH) (=exp(-itH) exp sH) for z (= t + is) in $\mathbb{C}_-$. Note that for such z, $\|\exp sH\| \leq 1$ (since $s \leq 0$ and $H \geq 0$) from spectral theory; so that $\|U_z\| = \|U_t \exp sH\| \leq 1$.

For the continuity and analyticity properties of $z \to U_z$, we shall need the following:

Lemma 1. <u>If (f_n) is a sequence of continuous complex-valued functions on $\mathbb{R}$ which converges pointwise to f, and $|f_n(t)| \leq K$ for all n and all real t, then $f_n(H)$ tends strongly to f(H), for each self-adjoint operator H.</u>

Proof. From the version of the Spectral Theorem noted, we may assume that H is multiplication by some (possibly, unbounded) measurable function h on $\mathcal{L}_2(X)$ and $f_n(H)$ is multiplication by $f_n \circ h$ (a bounded measurable function; so that there is no question of 'domain'). With g in $\mathcal{L}_2(X)$, we want to show that $(f_n \circ h) \cdot g$ tends to $(f \circ h) \cdot g$ in $\mathcal{L}_2(X)$ (i.e., in the mean of order 2). Now, $|(f_n \circ h) \cdot g| \leq K \cdot g$ and $(f_n \circ h) \cdot g$ tends to $(f \circ h) \cdot g$ almost everywhere (since $|f_n(t)| \leq K$ and f_n tends to f pointwise). From a form of the Lebesque Dominated Convergence Theorem [5; Corollary 16, p. 151], $(f_n \circ h) \cdot g$ tends to $(f \circ h) \cdot g$ in the mean of order 2.

Using the notation established preceding the lemma above, the continuity and analyticity properties of $z \to U_z$ we need are contained in:

Lemma 2. <u>If</u> $f(z) = ((\exp -izB)AU_{-z}\phi,\psi)$, <u>for</u> z <u>in</u> $\mathbb{C}_+$, <u>and</u> $g(z) = (U_z A(\exp izB)\phi,\psi)$, <u>for</u> z <u>in</u> $\mathbb{C}_-$, <u>with</u> ϕ <u>and</u> ψ <u>vectors in</u> $\mathcal{H}$ <u>and</u> B <u>a bounded operator on</u> $\mathcal{H}$; <u>then</u> f <u>and</u> g <u>are continuous on</u> $\mathbb{C}_+$ <u>and</u> $\mathbb{C}_-$ <u>and analytic in</u> $\mathbb{C}_+^o$ <u>and</u> $\mathbb{C}_-^o$, <u>respectively</u>.

Proof. We begin by showing that $z \to (U_z\phi,\psi)$ is anylytic in $\mathbb{C}_-^o$. With z_o in $\mathbb{C}_-^o$, we wish to establish that $[(U_z\phi,\psi) - (U_{z_o}\phi,\psi)](z - z_o)^{-1}$ $(=((\exp -izH - \exp -iz_oH)(z - z_o)^{-1}\phi,\psi))$ tends to a limit as z tends to z_o. This follows by applying Lemma 1 to the functions f_n defined on $\mathbb{R}$ by: $f_n(t) = (\exp -iz_nt - \exp -iz_ot)(z_n - z_o)^{-1}$ for $t \geqslant 0$ and $f_n(t) = 0$ for $t \leqslant 0$, where (z_n) is a sequence of complex numbers, tending to z_o $(= t_o + is_o)$, with $0 < |z_n - z_o| < \frac{-s_o}{2}$. To apply Lemma 1, we note that each f_n is continuous on $\mathbb{R}$, $f_n(t) \to -it \exp -iz_ot$ as $n \to \infty$ for each positive real t (by differentiability of $\exp -izt$ at z_o), and that $|f_n(t)| \leqslant -2(s_oe)^{-1}$ for all n and t. For this last inequality, with $t > 0$ we have:

$$|f_n(t)| = \frac{|(\exp -z_ot)(\exp -i(z_n - z_o)t - 1)|}{|z_n - z_o|}$$

$$\leqslant \frac{(\exp s_ot)(\exp|(z_n - z_o)t| - 1)}{|z_n - z_o|}$$

$$\leqslant (\exp s_ot)\left(t + \frac{|z_n - z_o|t^2}{2!} + \frac{|z_n - z_o|^2t^3}{3!} + \cdots\right)$$

$$\leqslant (t \exp s_ot)\exp|z_n - z_o|t \leqslant (t \exp s_ot)\exp - \frac{s_ot}{2}$$

$$= t \exp \frac{s_ot}{2}.$$

Our inequality follows, now, from the fact that, with $a < 0$, $t \to t \exp at$ has an absolute maximum on the positive t-axis at $t = -a^{-1}$, and that maximum is $-(ae)^{-1}$.

Note, next, that $z \to U_z$ is strong-operator continuous on $\mathbb{C}_-$. To prove this, we apply Lemma 1, again, this time to the functions f_n defined by: $f_n(t) = \exp -iz_n t$ for $t \geq 0$, and $f_n(t) = 1$ for $t < 0$, where (z_n) is a sequence in $\mathbb{C}_-$ tending to z_o. To apply Lemma 1, we observe that $|f_n(t)| \leq 1$ for all n and real t; while $f_n(t) \to \exp -iz_o t$ as $n \to \infty$ for $t \geq 0$, and $f_n(t) \to 1$ as $n \to \infty$ for $t < 0$. Lemma 1 allows us to conclude that $f_n(H)\phi = U_{z_n}\phi$ tends to $U_{z_o}\phi$ for each ϕ in $\mathcal{H}$, from which the strong-operator continuity of $z \to U_z$ on $\mathbb{C}_-$ follows.

To prove the analyticity of f in $\overset{\circ}{\mathbb{C}}_+$, note that

$$(f(z)-f(z_o))(z-z_o)^{-1} = (z-z_o)^{-1}[((\exp -izB - \exp -iz_oB)AU_{-z}\phi,\psi) + ((\exp -iz_oB)A(U_{-z}-U_{-z_o})\phi,\psi)] ,$$

and that

$$\|(\exp -izB - \exp -iz_oB)(z-z_o)^{-1} + iB \exp -iz_oB\|$$

$$= \|(-iB\exp -iz_oB)\left(\frac{-iB}{2!}(z-z_o) + \frac{(-iB)^2(z-z_o)^2}{3!} + \cdots\right)\|$$

$$\leq \|B \exp -iz_oB\| \cdot \|B\| \cdot |z-z_o| \left(\frac{1}{2!} + \frac{\|B\| \cdot |z-z_o|}{3!} + \frac{\|B\|^2 |z-z_o|^2}{4!} + \cdots\right) \leq$$

$$\leq \|B \exp -iz_oB\| \cdot \|B\| (\exp(\|B\| \cdot |z-z_o|))|z-z_o| \to 0 \text{ as } z \to z_o .$$

As just proved, $U_{-z}\phi \to U_{-z_o}\phi$ as $z \to z_o$ (z in $\mathbb{C}_+$).

Thus

$(z-z_o)^{-1}((\exp -izB - \exp -iz_oB)AU_{-z}\phi,\psi) \to -i((B \exp -iz_oB)AU_{-z_o}\phi,\psi)$

as $z \to z_o$. Letting ψ' be $A^*(\exp -iz_oB)^*\psi$,

$(z-z_o)^{-1}((\exp -iz_oB)A(U_{-z} - U_{-z_o})\phi,\psi) = (z-z_o)^{-1}((U_{-z} - U_{-z_o})\phi,\psi')$;

and, from the differentiability of $(U_{-z}\phi,\psi)$ at $-z_o$ in $\overset{o}{\mathbb{C}}_-$ established at the outset, $(z-z_o)^{-1}((U_{-z}-U_{-z_o})\phi,\psi')$ tends to a limit as $z \to z_o$.

Thus $(f(z) - f(z_o))(z-z_o)^{-1}$ tends to a limit as z tends to z_o in $\overset{o}{\mathbb{C}}_+$; and f is anylytic in $\overset{o}{\mathbb{C}}_+$.

For the analyticity of g in $\overset{o}{\mathbb{C}}_-$, note that

$(z-z_o)^{-1}(g(z)-g(z_o)) = (z-z_o)^{-1}[(U_zA(\exp izB - \exp iz_oB)\phi,\psi)$

$+ ((U_z-U_{z_o})A(\exp iz_oB)\phi,\psi)]$. Again, by analyticity of $z \to (U_z\phi',\psi')$, $(z-z_o)^{-1}((U_z-U_{z_o})A(\exp iz_oB)\phi,\psi)$ tends to a limit as z tends to z_o in $\overset{o}{\mathbb{C}}_-$. As before, $(z-z_o)^{-1}(\exp izB - \exp iz_oB)$ tends, in norm to $iB \exp iz_oB$; while U_z tends strongly to U_{z_o}, as z tends to z_o in $\mathbb{C}_-$. From the inequality,

$$\|(U_zT_z - U_{z_o}T_{z_o})\psi\| \leq \|U_z(T_z - T_{z_o})\psi\| + \|(U_z - U_{z_o})T_{z_o}\psi\|,$$

U_zT_z tends strongly to $U_{z_o}T_{z_o}$, when U_z tends strongly to U_{z_o}, $\|U_z\| \leq 1$, and T_z tends to T_{z_o} in norm (or just, strongly). Thus $(z-z_o)^{-1}$ $U_zA(\exp izB - \exp iz_oB)\phi \to iU_{z_o}AB(\exp iz_oB)\phi$ as $z \to z_o$ in $\overset{o}{\mathbb{C}}_-$; and g is anylytic in $\overset{o}{\mathbb{C}}_-$. The continuity of f on $\mathbb{C}_+$, follows from the (norm, hence) strong continuity of $z \to A^*(\exp -izB)^*$ and that of $z \to U_{-z}$ on $\mathbb{C}_+$; while that of g on $\mathbb{C}_-$ follows from the above inequality with T_z replaced by $\exp izB$.

3. ENERGY AS AN OBSERVABLE IN THE VACUUM THEORY

The first illustrative theorem (related to [1; Prop. 2] and appearing in [6; Theorem 11] essentially with its present proof--th ough, here, with the possibility of an unbounded generator) follows.

Theorem 3. *If* $\mathcal{R}$ *is a von Neumann algebra*, $t \to U_t (= \exp -itH)$ *a strongly continuous, one-parameter, unitary group, both acting on the Hilbert space* $\mathcal{H}$; *and* ψ_o *is a unit vector in* $\mathcal{H}$ *such that:*

(i) $U_t A U_{-t} \in \mathcal{R}$, *for each* A *in* $\mathcal{R}$ *and all real* t,

(ii) $H \geq 0$,

(iii) $H\psi_o = 0$

(iv) $\mathcal{R}\psi_o$ *is dense in* $\mathcal{H}$;

then $U_t \in \mathcal{R}$ *for all* t.

Before beginning the proof, we note that, aside from the general physical interpretation described in §2, condition (iii) is the assumption that the system has a state of (lowest) 0-energy--a type of "vacuum state". It is a crucial assumption for the argument we give; though, the result of the next section (Borcher's Theorem) removes this assumption (in essence). Condition (iv) is a normalizing assumption which permits us to draw the strong (and unphysical) conclusion that $U_t \in \mathcal{R}$. Without this assumption (though replaced by the condition that ψ_o has "contact" with all of $\mathcal{R}$--mathematically, that ψ_o has "central support" I relative to $\mathcal{R}$), we could conclude the more physical result: each α_t is inner. As far as the conclusion is concerned, it amounts to the fact that H (identified with the "total energy" of the system) is observable. Since H is (generally) unbounded, we do not expect to establish that H itself lies in $\mathcal{R}$. Knowing that each U_t is in $\mathcal{R}$, we can conclude (from Spectral Theory) that all the bounded functions of H lie in $\mathcal{R}$.

Proof of Theorem 3. From Lemma 2 and the observations preceding it, g defined on $\mathbb{C}_-$ by: $g(z) = (U_z A\psi_o, A'\psi_o)$, with A and A' self-adjoint operators in $\mathcal{R}$ and $\mathcal{R}'$, respectively, is continuous on $\mathbb{C}_-$ and analytic in $\mathbb{C}_-^o$ (taking B to be 0 in the definition of g in Lemma 2). Moreover, for real t,

$$g(t) = (U_t A\psi_o, A'\psi_o) = (A'U_t AU_{-t}\psi_o, \psi_o) = (U_t AU_{-t}A'\psi_o, \psi_o)$$

$$= (A'\psi_o, U_t A\psi_o) = \overline{g(t)},$$

noting that $U_t\psi_o = \psi_o$ for all t, since $H\psi_o = 0$ (and applying the Spectral Theorem). Thus g is real on the real axis and the Schwarz Reflection Principle (cf. [15; §4.5, pp. 155-157]) applies to guarantee the existence of an entire function G such that $G(z) = g(z) = \overline{G(\bar{z})}$ for z in $\mathbb{C}_-$. We have

$$|G(z)| = |G(\bar{z})| = |g(z)| \leq ||U_z|| \cdot ||A\psi_o|| \cdot ||A'\psi_o|| \leq ||A\psi_o|| \cdot ||A'\psi_o||,$$

for z in $\mathbb{C}_-$. Liouville's Theorem applies; and we conclude that G and g are constant. In particular,

$$g(0) = (A\psi_o, A'\psi_o) = g(t) = (U_t A\psi_o, A'\psi_o) = (A\psi_o, U_{-t}A'U_t\psi_o).$$

Thus $(A\psi_o, (A' - U_{-t}A'U_t)\psi_o) = 0$, for all self-adjoint A in $\mathcal{R}$, self-adjoint A' in $\mathcal{R}'$ and real t. Since $\mathcal{R}$ contains the adjoint of each operator in it, using the decomposition of an operator as the sum of a self-adjoint and a skew-adjoint operator, we see that the same equality holds for each A in $\mathcal{R}$. From the fact that $\mathcal{R}\psi_o$ is dense in $\mathcal{H}$ (condition (iv)), we conclude that $(A' - U_{-t}A'U_t)\psi_o = 0$. With T in $\mathcal{R}$,

$$0 = T(A' - U_{-t}A'U_t)\psi_o = (A'T - U_{-t}U_tTU_{-t}A'U_t)\psi_o$$

$$= (A'T - U_{-t}A'U_tT)\psi_o = (A' - U_{-t}A'U_t)T\psi_o \; .$$

Again, since $\mathcal{R}\psi_o$ is dense in $\mathcal{H}$, $A' - U_{-t}A'U_t = 0$. Thus $U_tA' = A'U_t$ for each self-adjoint A' in $\mathcal{R}'$; and $U_t \in (\mathcal{R}')'$ (= $\mathcal{R}$) for each real t.

4. ENERGY AS AN OBSERVABLE WITHOUT A VACUUM

In [3], Borchers shows that the assumption of the existence of a vacuum state (condition (iii) of Theorem 3) can be dropped (with the consequent weakening of the conclusion to the automorphisms being "inner"). He does this in the context of the 'local ring' formulation of quantum field theory and for representations of n-parameter rather than one-parameter groups. His argument is a several complex variable extension and strengthening of that of Theorem 3. The argument is aimed at a reduction to the case where the representation is norm (rather than, strong-operator) continuous. With this reduction accomplished, Borchers cites the Derivation Theorem [6, 7, 11], together with several von Neumann algebra lemmas which allow him to pass from the norm continuous to the strong-operator continuous case, to complete his proof. (In [4], Dell'Antonio proves the Borchers result in the context of automorphisms without the unitary representation assumed - paraphrasing the 'positive spectrum' condition suitably for this situation.)

In the following adaptation of Borchers' argument to the one-parameter (and one-complex variable) case, the passage from the norm continuous to the strong-operator continuous representation is effected by an earlier stronger application of the Derivation Theorem, and a positive spectrum conclusion is drawn.

Theorem 4. (Borchers) *If* $\mathcal{R}$ *is a von Neumann algebra and* $t \to U_t$ $(= \exp -itH)$ *is a strongly continuous, one-parameter, unitary group, both acting on the Hilbert space* $\mathcal{H}$, *such that:*

(i) *for each* A *in* $\mathcal{R}$ *and real* t, $U_t A U_{-t} \in \mathcal{R}$,

(ii) $H \geq 0$;

then there is a positive self-adjoint H_o *such that* $U_t A U_{-t} = V_t A V_{-t}$, *for each* A *in* $\mathcal{R}$ *and real* t, *where* $V_t = \exp -itH_o$ *and* V_t *lies in* $\mathcal{R}$ *for all real* t.

Proof. Let $\{E_\lambda\}$ be the spectral resolution of H and G_λ be the orthogonal projection on the closure of $\mathcal{R}' E_\lambda(\mathcal{H})$. Then G_λ lies in $\mathcal{R}$, since G_λ commutes with $\mathcal{R}'$. From (i), $U_t \mathcal{R}' U_{-t} = \mathcal{R}'$; so that $U_t \mathcal{R}' E_\lambda(\mathcal{H}) = U_t \mathcal{R}' U_{-t} U_t E_\lambda(\mathcal{H}) = \mathcal{R}' E_\lambda(U_t \mathcal{H}) = \mathcal{R}' E_\lambda(\mathcal{H})$. Since this holds, as well, for $U_{-t} (= U_t^*)$, $U_t G_\lambda = G_\lambda U_t$, for all real t; and $G_\lambda A G_\lambda \to U_t G_\lambda A G_\lambda U_{-t}$ $(= \alpha_t(G_\lambda A G_\lambda))$ defines an automorphism α_t of $G_\lambda \mathcal{R} G_\lambda$. Moreover $t \to \alpha_t$ is a one-parameter group, is norm continuous, that is

$$\|\alpha_t - \iota\| \; (= \sup\{ \|\alpha_t(G_\lambda A G_\lambda) - G_\lambda A G_\lambda\| : \|G_\lambda A G_\lambda\| \leq 1, \ A \text{ in } \mathcal{R} \}) \to 0$$

as $t \to 0$, where ι is the identity automorphism of $G_\lambda \mathcal{R} G_\lambda$.

Suppose, for the moment, that we have established this norm continuity. Then, from [8; Lemma 2], there is a self-adjoint operator H_λ in $G_\lambda \mathcal{R} G_\lambda$ with the property that $(\exp -itH_\lambda) G_\lambda A G_\lambda (\exp itH_\lambda) = U_t G_\lambda A G_\lambda U_{-t}$, for each A in $\mathcal{R}$ and all real t. Since $G_1 \leq G_2$ and

$$(\exp -itH_2) G_1 A G_1 (\exp itH_2) = (\exp -itH_1) G_1 A G_1 (\exp itH_1)$$

for all real t and all A in $\mathfrak{R}$; $H_2G_1 - H_1$ lies in the center, $\mathfrak{C}G_1$ of $G_1\mathfrak{R}G_1$, where $\mathfrak{C}$ is the center of $\mathfrak{R}$.. Say $H_2G_1 - H_1 = C_1G_1$, with C_1 in $\mathfrak{C}$. Let K_2 be $H_2 - C_1G_2$. As C_1G_2 is in the center of $G_2\mathfrak{R}G_2$, K_2 is in $G_2\mathfrak{R}G_2$; and

$$(\exp -itK_2)G_2AG_2(\exp itK_2) = (\exp -itH_2)G_2AG_2(\exp itH_2)$$

for all real t and all A in $\mathfrak{R}$. In addition, $K_2G_1 = H_2G_1 - C_1G_1 = H_1$. Continuing in this way, we find K_n in $G_n\mathfrak{R}G_n$, for each positive integer n, such that

$$(\exp -itK_n)G_nAG_n(\exp itK_n) = (\exp -itH_n)G_nAG_n(\exp itH_n)$$

for all real t and all A in $\mathfrak{R}$, and $K_nG_{n-1} = K_{n-1}$. The (simple) lemma following this proof shows that there is a self-adjoint operator K affiliated with $\mathfrak{R}$ (i.e. having all bounded functions in $\mathfrak{R}$) such that $KG_n = K_n$, for all n. Then

$$(\exp -itK)A(\exp itK) = (\exp -itH)A(\exp itH) ,$$

since G_n tends strongly to I as $n \to \infty$.

** The spectral measure F for K has range consisting of projections $F(\Omega)$ in $\mathfrak{R}$. Replacing A by $F(\Omega)$ in the preceding equality, we have $F(\Omega) = (\exp -itH)F(\Omega)(\exp itH)$. Thus $(\exp itH)(\exp -itK) = \exp it(H-K)$ (from the spectral theory described in §2); and $(\exp it(H-K))A = A\exp it(H-K)$ for all real t and all A in $\mathfrak{R}$.

** This paragraph, which makes more use of the theory of von Neumann algebras- particularly 'central carriers', may be ignored if the reader is prepared to take K as H_o and neglect the conclusion "$H_o \geq 0$".

It follows that $H - K$ $(= T')$ is affiliated with $\mathcal{R}'$; and $K + T'$ $(= H) \geq 0$. With $\{N'_\lambda\}$ the spectral resolution of T' and $F_m = F([-m,m])$, $F_m(K + T')N'_n \geq$ As $TN'_n \leq nN'_n$, $0 \leq F_m(K + T')N'_n \leq F_m(K + nF_m)N'_n$. Now $F_mK + nF_m$ is in $\mathcal{R}$; and the mapping $AN'_n \to AP_n$ of $\mathcal{R}N'_n$ onto $\mathcal{R}P_n$, where P_n is the central carrier of N'_n, is a *-isomorphism. Hence $0 \leq (F_mK + nF_m)P_n$. Letting $m \to \infty$, we see that $(K + nI)P_n \geq 0$. With Q_j the projection $P_j - P_{j-1}$ (in $\mathcal{C}$), the sequence $\Sigma_{j=1}^{n} jQ_j$ $(=C_n)$ of self-adjoint operators in $\mathcal{C}$ has the propertie $C_nP_{n-1} = C_{n-1}$ and $(K + C_n)P_n \geq 0$. From Lemma 5 (following), there is a self-adjoint operator C, affiliated with $\mathcal{C}$, such that $CP_n = C_n$ for each n. Thus, $K + C \geq 0$, since $(K + C)P_n = (K + C_n)P_n \geq 0$ and P_n $(\geq N'_n)$ tends strongl to I as n tends to ∞. Taking H_o to be $K + C$,

$$(\exp\text{-}itH_o)A(\exp itH_o) = (\exp\text{-}itK)A(\exp itK) = (\exp\text{-}itH)A(\exp itH),$$

for all real t and all A in $\mathcal{R}$; and $\exp\text{-}itH_o$ $(= V_t)$ is in $\mathcal{R}$.

It remains to prove that $t \to \alpha_t$ is norm continuous. We write G for G_λ, E for E_λ and let $W_z = E\exp(-izHE)$. Note that W_z is defined for all z, and $||W_z|| \leq \exp(|\mathcal{Im}\, z|\lambda)$ since $||HE|| \leq \lambda$. With $A'_1, \ldots, A'_n$; $B'_1, \ldots, B'_m$ in $\mathcal{R}'$, let ϕ be $\Sigma_k A'_k E\phi_k$ and ψ be $\Sigma_j B'_j E\psi_j$. Define f on $\mathbb{C}_+$ by:

$$f(z) = \Sigma_{j,k}\,(W_zAU_{-z}B'^*_jA'_kE\phi_k, \psi_j),$$

and g on $\mathbb{C}_-$ by:

$$g(z) = \Sigma_{j,k}\,(U_zAW_{-z}\phi_k, A'^*_kB'_jE\psi_j).$$

Note that

$$|f(z)| \leq ||W_z||\,\Sigma_{j,k}\,||A|| \cdot ||B'^*_jA'_kE\phi_k|| \cdot ||\psi_j|| \leq m_+\exp(|\mathcal{Im}\, z|\lambda)$$

and

$$|g(z)| \leq \|W_{-z}\| \Sigma_{j,k} \|A\| \cdot \|A_k'^*B_j'E\psi_j\| \cdot \|\phi_k\| \leq m_- \exp(|\mathcal{Im}\, z|\lambda) .$$

Since $W_t = EU_t$, for t real:

$$f(t) = \Sigma_{j,k} (W_t AU_{-t}B_j'^*A_k'E\phi_k, \psi_j) = \Sigma_{j,k} (EU_t AU_{-t}B_j'^*A_k'E\phi_k, \psi_j)$$

$$= \Sigma_{j,k} (U_t AU_{-t}A_k'E\phi_k, B_j'E\psi_j) = (U_t AU_{-t}\phi, \psi) = g(t) .$$

From Lemma 2, f and g are continuous on and analytic interior to $\mathcal{C}_+$ and $\mathcal{C}_-$, respectively (with B of that lemma taken, here, as HE). The Schwarz Reflection Principle tells us that F_o, defined as f on $\mathcal{C}_+$ and g on $\mathcal{C}_-$, is entire. Moreover, $|F_o(z)| \leq m \exp(|s|\lambda)$, where $z = t + is$ and $m = \max\{m_+, m_-\}$; while $|F_o(t)| \leq \|GAG\| \cdot \|\phi\| \cdot \|\psi\|$, for real t.

Letting $h_-(z)$ be $F_o(z) \exp -iz\lambda$; h_- is entire, $|h_-|$ is bounded by m on $\mathcal{C}_-$ and by $\|GAG\| \cdot \|\phi\| \cdot \|\psi\|$ on the real axis. Thus h_- is $O(\exp r\gamma)$ with $\gamma = 0$ on $\mathcal{C}_-$; and the Phragmen-Lindelöf Theorem (cf. [2; Theorem 1.4.2]) yields

$$|h_-(z)| = |F_o(z)| \exp s\lambda \leq \|GAG\| \cdot \|\phi\| \cdot \|\psi\| ,$$

for all z in $\mathcal{C}_-$. Similarly, if $h_+(z) = F_o(z) \exp iz\lambda$,

$$|h_+(z)| = |F_o(z)| \exp - s\lambda \leq \|GAG\| \cdot \|\phi\| \cdot \|\psi\| ,$$

for all z in $\mathcal{C}_+$. Hence, for all z in $\mathcal{C}$,

$$|F_o(z)| \leq \|GAG\| \cdot \|\phi\| \cdot \|\psi\| \exp |s|\lambda .$$

Defining $F(z)$ to be $(F_o(z) - F_o(0))(2\|GAG\| \cdot \|\phi\| \cdot \|\psi\| \exp \lambda)^{-1}$;

F is entire, $F(0) = 0$, and $|F(z)| \leq 1$ for $|z| \leq 1$. From Schwarz's Lemma, $|F(z)| \leq |z|$ for $|z| \leq 1$; so that for a dense set of vectors ϕ and ψ in $G(\mathcal{H})$,

$$|((U_t GAGU_{-t} - GAG)\phi, \psi)| \leq 2|t| \cdot \|GAG\| \cdot \|\phi\| \cdot \|\psi\| \exp \lambda .$$

Thus,

$$\|\alpha_t(GAG) - GAG\| \leq 2|t| \cdot \|GAG\| \exp \lambda \ ;$$

and the norm continuity of $t \to \alpha_t$ follows.

The existence of H_o such that $H_o G_n = H_n$, used to complete the preceding argument, follows from:

Lemma 5. <u>If (G_n) is an increasing sequence of projections and (H_n) is a sequence of bounded self-adjoint operators such that $H_n G_n = H_n$ and $H_n G_{n-1} = H_{n-1}$ for all n, then there is a self-adjoint operator H (bounded if and only if the H_n are uniformly bounded) such that $HG_n = H_n$ for all n.</u>

Proof. Since $H_m G_n = H_m G_k G_n$ when $n \leq k \leq m$, it follows that $H_m G_n = H_n$ and $H_m H_n = H_n H_m$. Passing to a maximal abelian (von Neumann) algebra containing $\{G_n, H_n\}$ and its representation as the multiplication algebra of some measure space (X, m), we may assume that G_n is multiplication by g_n, the characteristic function of a measurable subset S_n of X and H_n is multiplication by the bounded real function h_n. The conditions on (G_n) and (H_n) imply that $S_n \subseteq S_{n+1}$ and $h_m g_n = h_n$. As a result, (h_m) converges almost everywhere to a measurable real function h multiplication by which corresponds to a self-adjoint operator H such that $HG_n = H_n$. Moreover, h is (essentially) bounded if and only if the h_m are uniformly (essentially) bounded; so that H is bounded if and only if the H_m are uniformly bounded.

5. A LITTLE REEH - SCHLIEDER THEOREM

The analytic techniques and arguments of quantum field theory can be modified, again, to give a theorem of the Reeh - Schlieder type [10, 16; Théorème 2.1] in the simplified one-variable situation. For its statement, we shall need some terminology. If $t \to \exp{-itH}$ is a strongly continuous, one-parameter, unitary group on $\mathcal{H}$ (with H self-adjoint), a vector ψ in $\mathcal{H}$ is said to correspond to a state of *finite energy* (relative to H), when $E\psi = \psi$ for some projection E commuting with H such that HE is bounded.

We shall use the notation ' $[\mathcal{F}\psi]$ ', with $\mathcal{F}$ a family of bounded operators on $\mathcal{H}$, to denote the closed linear subspace of $\mathcal{H}$ spanned by vectors of the form $T\psi$, with T in $\mathcal{F}$.

Theorem 6. (Little Reeh - Schlieder) *If $\mathcal{U}_o$ is a C*-algebra and $t \to \exp{-itH}$ $(=U_t)$, with $H \geq 0$, is a one parameter unitary group acting on the Hilbert space $\mathcal{H}$; then, denoting by $\mathcal{U}_\mathcal{S}$ the set $\{U_t A U_{-t}: A$ in $\mathcal{U}_o$, t in $\mathcal{S}\}$ where $\mathcal{S}$ is a subset of $\mathbb{R}$, we have $[\mathcal{U}_\mathcal{S}\psi] = [\mathcal{U}_\mathbb{R}\psi]$ for each ψ of finite energy in $\mathcal{H}$ and each subset $\mathcal{S}$ of $\mathbb{R}$ with non-null interior.*

Proof. Since $\mathcal{S}$ has non-null interior, it contains some open interval (a, b). Clearly, $[\mathcal{U}_{(a,b)}\psi] \subseteq [\mathcal{U}_\mathcal{S}\psi] \subseteq [\mathcal{U}_\mathbb{R}\psi]$; so that it will suffice to establish our assertion for $\mathcal{S}$ an open interval. We show that $[\mathcal{U}_\mathbb{R}\psi] \subseteq [\mathcal{U}_{(a,b)}\psi]$, by proving that ϕ is orthogonal to $[\mathcal{U}_\mathbb{R}\psi]$, if ϕ (in $\mathcal{H}$) is orthogonal to $[\mathcal{U}_{(a,b)}\psi]$.

Suppose, then, that $(U_t A U_{-t}\psi, \phi) = 0$ for all t in (a,b) and A in

$\mathfrak{U}_o$. Since ψ corresponds to a state of finite energy (relative to H), there is a projection E such that HE (= EH) is bounded and $E\psi = \psi$. Let W_z be E exp (-izHE), for all complex z. Define g by: $g(z) = (U_z A W_{-z} \psi, \phi)$, for z in $\mathbb{C}_-$. Applying Lemma 2 (with HE replacing B), we have that g is continuous on $\mathbb{C}_-$ and analytic in $\mathbb{C}_-^o$. Note that

$$g(t) = (U_t A W_{-t}\psi, \phi) = (U_t AE \exp(itHE)\, \psi, \phi)$$
$$= (U_t A \exp(itH)\, E\psi, \phi) = (U_t A U_{-t}\psi, \phi) ,$$

for real t; so that $g(t) = 0$ for t in (a, b). Combining this last information with the analyticity of g in $\mathbb{C}_-^o$ and continuity on $\mathbb{C}_-$ (for example, using the Schwarz Reflection Principle on g in the strip $a \leq \mathcal{R}e\, z \leq b$) tells us that $g(z) = 0$ for z in $\mathbb{C}_-$. In particular, $0 = g(t) = (U_t A U_{-t}\psi, \phi)$ for all real t and all A in $\mathfrak{U}_o$; so that ϕ is orthogonal to $[\mathfrak{U}_{\mathbb{R}}\, \psi]$, as we wanted to show.

University of Pennsylvania,

Philadelphia, Pennsylvania

REFERENCES

1. H. Araki, On the algebra of all local observables, Res. Inst. Math. Sci. Kyoto, No. 5 (1964), pp. 1-16.
2. R. Boas, Entire Functions, Academic Press Inc., New York, 1954.
3. H. Borchers, Energy and momentum as observables in quantum field theory, Commun. Math. Phys., 2(1966), pp. 49-54.
4. G. Dell'Antonio, On some groups of automorphisms of physical observables, Commun. Math. Phys., 2(1966), pp. 384-397.
5. N. Dunford and J. Schwartz, Linear Operators, Part I, Interscience Publishers Inc., New York, 1958.
6. R. Kadison, Derivations of operator algebras, Ann. of Math., 83(1966), pp. 280-293.
7. R. Kadison and J. Ringrose, Derivations of operator group algebras, Amer. J. Math., 88(1966), pp. 562-576.
8. R. Kadison and J. Ringrose, Derivations and automorphisms of operator algebras, Commun. Math. Phys., 4(1967), pp. 32-63.
9. J. von Neumann, Zur Algebra der Funktionaloperationen und Theorie der Normalen Operatoren, Math. Ann., 102(1929), pp. 370-427.
10. H. Reeh and S. Schlieder, Bemerkungen zur Unitäräquivalenz von Lorentzinvarianten Feldern, Nuovo Cimento, 22(1961), p. 1051.
11. S. Sakai, Derivations of W*-algebras, Ann. of Math., 83(1966), pp. 273-279.
12. I. Segal, Decompositions of operator algebras II, Memoirs Amer. Math. Soc., no. 9(1951), pp. 1-66.

13. R. Streater and A. Wightman, PCT, Spin & Statistics, And All That, W. A. Benjamin Inc., New York, 1964.

14. M. Stone, On one parameter unitary groups in Hilbert space, Ann. of Math., 33(1932), pp. 643-648.

15. E. Titchmarsh, The Theory of Functions, Oxford Univ., London 1939.

16. A. Wightman, La théorie quantique locale et la théorie quantique des champs, Ann. Inst. Henri Poincaré, 1(1964), pp. 403-420.

The Mathematical Theory of Quantum Fields

by

Irving E. Segal

Lecture presented at the

American University, Washington, D. C., 7 December 1968

Introduction.

Since it is absolutely hopeless to give here a detailed account of anything more than the tiniest fragment of the mathematical theory of quantum fields, I shall not attempt anything in the way of a detailed exposition of the fine structure of the theory. Instead, I shall concentrate on trying to present an overall view, basically mathematical but with significant reference to the qualitative physical situation, of the essential scientific architecture of the subject. I want to give at least some impression of the purely mathematically quite compelling and conceptually very simple and broadly relevant nature of the theory. Far from being a subject which is worth pursuing only to the extent that it produces analytically numbers which can be correlated with experimental laboratory measurements--a most worthy endeavor, but surely not the only or perhaps even main proper aim of mathematical physics, for in practice the empirical numbers can be obtained as easily and with greater assurance and sooner than the theoretical ones-- it is worth pursuing primarily because of its "great mathematical beauty," as Dirac himself once remarked. Indeed, quite recently connections have developed between quantum field theory and number theory, the Murray-von

Neumann theory of operator rings, the topology of manifolds--in addition to the less surprising but notably profound connections with probability in function space, group representation theory, and generalized function and differential equation theory. But I want also to trace briefly the key connections between the physically observed quantities, their theoretical counterparts according to conventional physics, and objective and natural mathematical notions. I want especially to discuss the S-operator (or S-matrix, as physicists like to call it), for it is less familiar to mathematicians than the energy operator, and yet even more fundamental from an observational standpoint, in high-energy processes, as well as mathematically a key object. Finally, I want to indicate briefly how the profound disfigurements to the mathematical beauty of quantum field theory provided by a vast clutter of so-called divergences of various sorts can be eliminated in the fundamental equations of the theory in a conceptually simple way--so that we deal today, at long last, with mathematically definite and natural questions, which will no doubt be resoluble in due course, and promise to give new and better ways to arrive at quantitative answers than the old widely-deplored and doubted but much used perturbative expansion.

Fields, processes, particles, and waves.

Theoretical physicists talk much about "fields," but it is hard to get a straight answer, from a mathematician's standpoint, to the question: what is a field? Years ago when I was first getting into the subject, and had an intense horror of vague, idealistic words which seemed to contribute only to rhetoric and not at all to the mathematical or observational content of the theory, I confronted Fermi with this blunt question. I was very much relieved that the great man did not respond that this was a stupid or irrelevant question, and that everyone that had any right to think about such matters knew of course what a field was, but appeared to take the question seriously. He stopped to think for a moment, and then responded that, in his judgement, "field" meant most basically the "occupation number formalism." This is a perfectly definite, non-metaphysical, matter, which one can treat along clear and natural purely mathematical lines, and I felt much reassured, if not technically enlightened. For whatever it may be worth, my experience has been that really outstanding theoretical physicists take a position which, when sympathetically and thoroughly analyzed and interpreted, is seen to be quite mathematical in spirit--even though they are in general unaware of this--although at the same time grammatically primitive and technically not infrequently quite incorrect.

The purpose of this little prelude has been to point up the limitations--at best--of attempting to construe physical terminology with the exactitude of mathematics, or of using a largely physical nomenclature. Instead I shall use to a maximal extent a lingua franca based on modern algebra, geometry, and analysis, and avoid the proliferations of scientific colloquialisms (of quite variable meaning, if any) which have grown up around "quantum field theory,"--so-called. On the other hand, at a certain stage it is crucial to develop a scientifically (but inevitably not mathematically) precise mathematical-physical dictionary, for the purpose of displaying the external relevance of the purely mathematical developments under discussion. Given the expositional axiom that a mathematical presentation must be made in a totally, rather than partially ordered way, it might be logical to postpone the correlation with theoretical physics until after the purely mathematical development. But given the present limitations of time and the probable interest of much of the audience in external relevance, as against intrinsic perfection, of the mathematics involved, I shall instead adopt the course of interpolating this material as asides and footnotes throughout the course of the mathematical development.

I begin therefore in a blunt mathematical way with the

Definition. Let $(\underline{L},A)$ be a pair consisting of a given real linear topological vector space $\underline{L}$, together with a given non-degenerate anti-symmetric form A on $\underline{L}$. An anti-symmetric process over $(\underline{L},A)$ is a pair $(\phi,\underline{K})$ consisting of a mapping ϕ from $\underline{L}$ to self-adjoint operators in the Hilbert space $\underline{K}$, satisfying the relations:
$x \to e^{i\phi(x)}$ is continuous, and

$$e^{i\phi(x)}e^{i\phi(y)} = e^{(i/2)A(x,y)}e^{i\phi(y)}e^{i\phi(x)} .$$

Parenthetically, this is what is also known as a "Weyl system," or "representation of the canonical commutation relations;" on occasion, it is called a "Bose-Einstein field" or "boson field;" the operators $\phi(x)$ are sometimes called "field variables." The salient mathematical fact is that when $\underline{L}$ is finite-dimensional, there is for given A a unique anti-symmetric quantum process, within unitary equivalence, and within the obvious flexibility of a change of multiplicity, i.e. the formation of a direct sum of copies of the process. This result, developed by Stone with the aim of correlating the Heisenberg and Schrödinger formulations of elementary quantum mechanics (which Schrödinger mistakenly believed he had done in a paper in which he had observed at length the isomorphism between l_2 and L_2), was established in its most cogent form in a beautiful paper by von Neumann in 1931. Parenthetically again, this result, developed primarily because of its quantum mechanical relevance, has turned out to be one of the most central and applicable results in harmonic analysis; together with the classical theorem of Stone on one-parameter groups, it implies the Plancherel theorem (though not vice versa), and has been quite useful in prediction, ergodic, and scattering theory. At any rate, the uniqueness conclusion turned out to be totally false when $\underline{L}$ is infinite-dimensional, even in the most regular cases. This disposed of a physical folk theorem, implicitly assumed in many of the early theoretical treatments of quantum fields, sometimes stated in the form: "any two (irreducible) representations of the canonical commutation relations are unitarily equivalent." On the other hand, the ultimate disposition of this folk theorem illustrates once again the extraordinary capacity of theoretical physics to embody a germ of eventual truth even when technically quite wrong. It turned out that there is a conceptually simple infinite-dimensional generalization of the classical Stone-von Neumann uniqueness theorem: the C*-algebras associated with any two anti-symmetric processes over the same pair--for short their Weyl algebras--are naturally algebraically isomorphic. I can't stop to define the Weyl algebra here, but will only remark that this was the beginning of the since substantiated notion that the temporal development of a quantum field is given in the first instance not necessarily by a one-parameter group of unitary operators, as in classical quantum mechanics, but by a one-parameter group of automorphisms of a C*-algebra. Since every automorphism of the algebra of all bounded operators on a Hilbert space is induced by some unitary operator, this C*-algebra could not consist of all bounded operators on any space; but it was in a certain sense locally identical with an algebra of all bounded operators.

Returning now to the purely mathematical development, the vast non-uniqueness which can take place in the infinite-dimensional case has in part to do with a lack of adequate mathematical structure or physical completeness on the part of the pair $(\underline{L},A)$. Usually there is given additionally a group G, and a continuous representation V of G by automorphisms of $(\underline{L},A)$, i.e. a continuous map $a \to V(a)$ of G into invertible linear transformations on $\underline{L}$ which preserve the form A. One may then make the

Definition. A covariant anti-symmetric process relative to the given system $(\underline{L},A,G,V(.))$ with the indicated properties is a system $(\phi,\underline{K},\Gamma(.))$, where $(\phi,\underline{K})$ is as before, and $\Gamma(.)$ is a continuous unitary representation of G on $\underline{K}$ such that

$$\Gamma(a)\phi(x)\Gamma(a)^{-1} = \phi(V(a)x) \quad .$$

A non-zero vector v in $\underline{K}$ is called an equilibrium (or stationary) state vector for the process provided $\Gamma(a)v = v$ for all $a \in G$. An anti-symmetric field relative to $(\underline{L},A,G,V(.))$ may here be defined as a system $(\phi,\underline{K},\Gamma(.),v)$ having all of the foregoing properties, and in addition the property that v is cyclic with respect to the operators $e^{i\phi(x)}$, $x \in \underline{L}$ and $\Gamma(a)$, $a \in G$.

There are many fewer anti-symmetric fields in this sense than there are anti-symmetric processes, provided G and V are sufficiently non-trivial, but there is still very far from being a unique one. For example, one of the simplest relevant cases is that in which (L,A) is derived from a given complex Hilbert space H by taking L as the real linear topological space underlying H, and $A(x,y) = \mathrm{Im}\langle x,y\rangle$; and in which V is a unitary representation of G on H. When G consists of all unitary operators on H, and V(a) = a, all anti-symmetric fields are known; there is a basic one-parameter continuum of distinct fields, plus in addition the mixtures in a certain sense of these fields, any such mixture being labeled by a probability measure on R^1. When G consists of the Poincaré (= inhomogeneous Lorentz) group, and V of any non-trivial unitary representation, it is an open question whether there are any anti-symmetric fields other than those just indicated. If $H = L_2(R^3)$, G is the euclidean group, and V gives the natural induced action of G on H, the determination and classification of the anti-symmetric processes is one of the central, as yet largely unsolved, questions of abstract equilibrium statistical mechanics; in any reasonable sense, the manifold of essentially distinct such processes (a notion readily transcribed mathematically in terms of pure state spaces of associated C*-algebras) is infinite-dimensional.

There is however a mathematically simple and physically classical further assumption which leads to a unique anti-symmetric field, namely that of the "positivity of the energy." In purely mathematical terms, the energy is the self-adjoint generator of the one parameter unitary group $\Gamma|T$, where T is a given one-parameter subgroup of G; identifying T with R^1 and denoting as $\Gamma(t)$ the corresponding unitary operator to $t \in R^1$, our dictionary dubs $\Gamma(t)$ "temporal displacement by t units." No matter; the important thing mathematically is the postulate, called "positivity of the energy," that the self-adjoint generator H of $\Gamma(.)$ be non-negative. Under mild regularity conditions--it is sufficient if $(\underline{L},A,G,V)$ be derived from a unitary representation of G on a complex Hilbert space, in the fashion earlier indicated, for example--there is then a unique system $(\phi,\underline{K},\Gamma(.),v)$--if any exists at all.

The temporal translation subgroup T plays an extremely distinctive role, both mathematically and physically, so much so that it is analytically advantageous to forget about the rest of the group G, until much later in the game. This not only makes the theory much more general--there are many interesting systems for which the relevant group is exactly or little more than T --but clarifies the relationship between the "dynamics," i.e. the theory associated with $\Gamma|T$, and the "kinematics," roughly the complementary theory associated with the restriction of Γ to the centralizer of T in G. In the so-called relativistic case, i.e. essentially that in which G is the Poincaré group, the final results will again necessarily be appropriately relativistic, even though developed entirely through consideration of the temporal translation subgroup; and one has a demonstration of the principle that the "dynamics supersedes the kinematics;" indeed, the kinematics may be trivial without qualitatively affecting the dynamical theory.

In these terms, one can summarize the situation as follows. Let a triple $(\underline{L},A,V(.))$ be called a "classical linear dynamical system" if V(.) is a continuous one-parameter group of linear transformations on the real linear topological vector space L, leaving invariant the non-degenerate continuous bilinear anti-symmetric form A on L, the topology being inducible from a positive definite real symmetric form on L; when L is finite-dimensional, this terminology is consistent with classical notions, e.g. as represented by Whittaker's Analytical Dynamics, but our concern here is primarily with the infinite-dimensional case. There then always exists an anti-symmetric process (ϕ, K) over (L,A) and a representation $\gamma(.)$ of T by automorphisms of the associated C*-algebra. In general, however, there will exist no adequately regular stationary state for the system (state here in the sense of positive normalized linear functional on a C*-algebra), or equivalently associated anti-symmetric field. Indeed, a necessary and sufficient condition that there should be a regular stationary state is that (L,A,V(.)) should be essentially "Hilbert," i.e. that L should be imbeddable as a dense subset of a complex Hilbert space in such a way that A is carried into the imaginary part of the inner product and V(.) becomes unitary. Relative to the representation associated with this stationary state, the one-parameter automorphism group of the C*-algebra is canonically unitarily implementable, and an anti-symmetric field in the sense of the earlier definition is obtained. In general, however, there will exist no positive-energy such field; a necessary and sufficient condition for this to exist is that the structure (L,A,V(.)) should be "Hilbertizable" so-to-speak as indicated, in such a way that the self-adjoint generator of the unitary group V(.) should be non-negative. If (and only if) the generator annihilates no non-zero vector, the associated positive-energy field is unique.

Now this has all been quite abstract, and perhaps a bit obscure, but there are only a few simple corollaries that I want to insist on, before giving some illustrative, and I hope refreshing examples. One is that the unique field finally attained in suitable cases--what physicists call, in various concrete manifestations, the "free field,"--is not something derived on a purely authoritarian or physical basis, but is uniquely determined by a very small number of mathematical assumptions corresponding to an extremely conservative physical position. Another is that the structure of this field has basically little, if anything, to do with the space-time continuum, which enters only as a means of labeling the elements of $\underline{L}$ --generally, but not at all necessarily, as the solution manifold of a given partial differential equation; for many purposes one needs only a group representation and an invariant bilinear form to get the theory rolling. The spatio-temporal significance of vectors in $\underline{L}$ becomes of primary importance only when "interacting" fields are involved. Finally, one of the most important principles of contemporary physics--the duality between waves and particles--is a purely mathematical corollary to the general structure of a positive-energy field. However it may ultimately be with non-linear field theories, there is very little doubt that the mathematical structure just delineated is a remarkably economical as well as sound and useful model for "free" or "non-interacting" particles or wave fields.

Let me first say how the theory goes on the basis of an abstract Hilbert space; then describe the simplest relativistic case, of a "scalar" field; and finally treat the conventionally most complicated, although physically best known, case of the Maxwell field.

Let $\underline{H}$ be a given complex Hilbert space, and U(.) a given positive-energy one-parameter unitary group on $\underline{H}$, leaving fixed no non-zero vector. The associated unique positive-energy anti-symmetric field $(\phi,\underline{K},\Gamma,v)$ may then be described, within unitary equivalence, as follows. First, $\underline{K}$ is the Hilbert space direct sum over all non-negative integers n of the symmetric tensor (Hilbert-space) product $\underline{H}_n$ of $\underline{H}$ with itself n times (when n = 0, the corresponding space is defined as one-dimensional; v is taken as any element of norm 1 in $\underline{H}_o$); $\Gamma'(V)$ for any unitary V on $\underline{H}$ is the canonically induced operator on $\underline{K}$; while $\Gamma(a) = \Gamma'(V(a))$. ϕ is a bit more complicated to describe, and the description is difficult to motivate, except by its success and its parallelism with familiar recurrence relations for Hermitefunctions, which are related to the special case when $\underline{H}$ is finite-dimensional. In brief, $\phi(x)$ has the form $2^{-(1/2)}(C(x) + C(x)^*)$, where C(x) acting on an n-tensor u transforms it into the symmetrized tensor product $x \times u$, multiplied by $(n+1)^{1/2}$.

One sees at a glance that the construction depends essentially only on the Hilbert space $\underline{H}$, and hardly at all on the given classical dynamics U(.). Γ' is easily seen to be a continuous unitary representation on $\underline{K}$ of the full unitary group on $\underline{H}$; as such it has an infinitesimal form $d\Gamma'$ applicable to arbitrary self-adjoint operators in $\underline{H}$. The essentially linear map $d\Gamma'$ (i.e. linear modulo the complications arising from the presence of unbounded operators) is of basic significance; if H is the generator of U(.)--physically, the so-called "single-particle," or "classical" hamiltonian--then $d\Gamma'(H)$ is the corresponding "field" hamiltonian. A distinctive feature of Γ'

essentially the positivity of the energy is that, $d\Gamma'(A) \geq 0$ if $A \geq 0$. For a projection P, it is easily seen that $d\Gamma(P)$ has non-negative integral eigenvalues, and for this reason, and its relations to $d\Gamma'(H)$ and similar operators, is appropriately construed as a particle number--more specifically, as "the number of particles whose wave function is in the range of P." In particular, $d\Gamma(I)$ is the "total number of particles," the conservation of which for free fields is simply a reflection of the commutativity of I with all other operators. Fermi's definition of "field" then relates to the following circumstance: if $\{P_\mu\}$ is a collection $\underline{C}$ of projections (or operators) on $\underline{H}$ generating a maximal abelian operator ring, then the $d\Gamma'(P_\mu)$, or rather their bounded functions for these are unbounded, generate a maximal abelian operator ring on $\underline{K}$. Speaking briefly, one observes in quantum mechanics at most such maximal abelian collections of "observables;" thus if $\{e_i\}$ is an ortho-normal basis in $\underline{H}$, and P_i the projection of $\underline{H}$ onto the one-dimensional subspace spanned by e_i, then the $N_i = d\Gamma(P_{e_i})$, which physically represent "the number of particles in the state having wave function e_i," form a complete set of observables for observations on the quantum field $\underline{K}$, i.e. the most that could be observed in a theoretically perfect experiment.

The "occupation numbers" N_i thus appear as very simple operators, and are indeed easily simultaneourly diagonalized, in the foregoing "particle" representation for a positive-energy field. On the other hand, the operators $\phi(x)$ are quite complicated, and it is non-trivial to show that they are self-adjoint and satisfy the commutation ("Weyl") relation indicated earlier. Still, if $\underline{H}'$ is a real-linear subspace of

$\underline{H}$ such that $\underline{H} = \underline{H}' + i\underline{H}'$, or equivalently if $\underline{H}'$ is a real linear subspace of $\underline{H}$ which is maximal with respect to the vanishing of the restriction to it of the form $\mathrm{Im}\langle .,. \rangle$, then the $\phi(x)$ for $x \varepsilon \underline{H}'$ form, like the occupation numbers, a complete commuting set, and so from an abstract phenomenological point of view are just as good as the occupation numbers. Indeed, the labeling of vectors in $\underline{K}$ in terms of the $\phi(x)$ for $x \varepsilon \underline{H}'$, for suitable subspaces $\underline{H}'$, represents the "wave," as opposed to earlier "particle" analysis of the field as is clearly visible from a specific analysis of the electro-magnetic or similar fields. The particle-wave duality arrived at in physics after centuries of doubt concerning the nature of light is, when stripped of metaphysics, simply an instance of the mathematical phenomenon just indicated, that the corpuscular observables on the one hand, and the undulatory ones on the other, each determine complete but quite disparate and incompatible sets of labels for the vectors in the state vector space $\underline{K}$. More specifically, each determines a maximal abelian algebra of bounded linear operators in $\underline{K}$, the two algebras having only the scalar operators in common, and the fundamental operators--the particle numbers $d\Gamma(P)$ on the one hand and the field strengths $\phi(x)$, $x \varepsilon \underline{H}'$, on the other, obeying commutation relations somewhat similar to the ones already indicated.

The simultaneous diagonalization of the field strengths $\phi(x)$, $x \varepsilon \underline{H}'$ is achieved by a different representation for a normal anti-symmetric field, i.e. the indicated unique one; "normal" is an appropriate designation not only because it is the commonly arising field, but also because it is a kind of quantum extension of the conventional normal probability measure; indeed, the generating function $\langle e^{i\phi(x)}v,v\rangle$, from which all quantitative features of the process can essentially be read off, has the form $e^{-(1/4)\|x\|^2}$. Furthermore, in the "wave" representation, so to speak, $\underline{K}$ is represented as $L_2(\underline{H}')$, relative to the normal probability measure in $\underline{H}'$. In this representation, v is simply the function identically 1 on $\underline{H}$; $\phi(x)$ for $x \varepsilon \underline{H}'$ is, within a constant factor, simply multiplication by the linear functional $\langle x,y\rangle$, acting on functionals of y ; but $\Gamma(V)$ (and so the occupation numbers) takes a relatively complicated form, except when V is a kinematical transformation. This wave representation will be seen to be very important in connection with interactions of quantum fields, for the description of the interaction process at finite times; complementarily, the particle representation described earlier is crucial for the description of the free fields at times so early or late as to be construed as $\pm\infty$ in the theory.

Example 1. "Quantization" of the differential equation

$$\Box\, \emptyset = c\emptyset \qquad (\phi(x) = \emptyset(\vec{x},t) \; ; \; \Box = -(\partial/\partial t)^2 + \Delta) \; .$$

The space $\underline{L}$ is here taken as the set of all real solutions of the indicated equation, of a prescribed degree of regularity; the final quantization is, within wide limits, independent of the precise degree of regularity which is required. Taking for specificity solutions which are C^∞ and have compact support as a function of the space variable $\vec{x}$ for each fixed time t, the fundamental anti-symmetric form A is given by the equation

$$A(\phi_1,\phi_2) = \int (\phi_1(\vec{x},t)\dot{\phi}_2(\vec{x},t) - \dot{\phi}_1(\vec{x},t)\phi_2(x,t))d\vec{x} \ ;$$

the indicated integral over space depends only speciously on the time; it is easily seen to be non-degenerate, and continuous in the topology defined by the pseudo-norms $\|\text{grad}\ \phi(.,t)\|_2$, $\|\phi(.,t)\|_2$, $\|\dot{\phi}(.,t)\|_2$ (which are equivalent for different t). It follows from the general theory that there exists an anti-symmetric process, which may be said to represent a quantization of the indicated equation, and for which temporal translation is represented by a one-parameter group of automorphisms of the associated Weyl (C^*)-algebra; indeed, the full Poincaré group can be seen to act as a group of such automorphisms. In general, however, there will be no regular stationary state, or equivalently, no concrete representation for the C^*-algebra as operators on a Hilbert space in which temporal translation is unitarily implemented, and a vector v of the earlier indicated type is present. This is exactly the case when $c < 0$; intuitively, it represents a certain extreme instability for the field or particles described by the equation, which indeed has had some recent consideration in the physical literature as a model for particles "moving faster than light;" the indicated result on the absence of a "regular" stationary state can be considered as a central theoretical fact underlying some of these heuristic considerations; physically speaking, such a particle would be unobservable, for all finite quantities associated with it would have vanishing expectation value (paradoxically, this is essentially the same as saying that with probability 1, the particle would end up at ∞ in space, and with infinite momentum, and so would be unobservable). The same phenomenon has a quite simple group-theoretical interpretation. The system $(\underline{L},A,V(.))$, where $V(t)$ is of course the operation of temporal translation defined by the differential equation, is complex Hilbertizable if and only if $c \geq 0$.

When $c \geq 0$, it is easily seen from a Fourier analysis or indeed otherwise (by methods applicable also to equations of the form

$$\Box \phi = c\phi + V\phi ,$$

where V is a given non-negative function--an example of an equation with only temporal translational invariance, to which the theory is directly applicable), that the unitary representation which results can be taken to have positive energy, and is then unique. This means that there then exists a unique anti-symmetric positive-energy field for the equation. Colloquially, this field is described as a "neutral scalar meson field" or a "Klein-Gordon" field, etc. when $V = 0$; or as such a field subjected to a type of external potential V in the general case.

One could almost as well have proceeded purely group-theoretically. The unitary representation of the Poincaré group associated with the differential equation $\Box \phi = c\phi$, $c \geq 0$, is easily seen to be irreducible, and is readily described independently, within unitary equivalence, without reference to differential equations or to the formulation of the vectors in the representation space as functions on space-time. It seems likely that one can do most, if not all, of the quantitative physics of free fields purely in terms of such a group representation; it would probably be quite interesting to do so; but when it comes to interacting fields, a differential equation and a spatio-temporal interpretation of the vectors in the representation space play an essential role.

I should like to treat interactions in terms of a specific example, that of quantum electrodynamics. It is in some ways the most troublesome from a foundational point of view, of all the familiar heuristic quantum fields; in particular the quantization of the Maxwell equations is treated in the literature as if it were basically exceptional, and requires ad hoc devices. On the other hand, quantum electro-dynamics is mathematically the most symmetrical and richly structured of all interacting fields yet treated at length in the literature, and at the same time the one which has had the closest contact with experimental numbers. Let me therefore briefly treat the quantization of the Maxwell equations. The quantization of the Dirac equations will be passed over for lack of time with the summary remarks that it requires a symmetric, rather than anti-symmetric process; and that otherwise, quite remarkebly, virtually every general property of anti-symmetric processes has a clearly identifiable analogue in the case of a symmetric process, the Weyl algebra being replaced by an infinite-dimensional Clifford algebra. For example, the uniqueness of the positive-energy field carries over; this result removes quantized hole theory from its original category of virtual metaphysics or its position as a successful and unchallenged hypothesis, as it stands in the existing physical literature, to a basically simple purely mathematical manifestation. Finally I shall discuss the quantization of the coupled Maxwell-Dirac equations.

Maxwell's equations may be taken in terms either of field strengths or of potentials; for the treatment of the coupling with the Dirac equation, the latter form is much more convenient, in spite of the more physical character of the field strengths. Briefly, the potentials A_j are functions on space-time satisfying the differential equation $\Box A_j = 0$ $(j = 0, 1, 2, 3)$, and certain additional restrictions which serve to pick out a convenient representative from the class of all potentials giving rise to the same field strengths; one convenient such restriction is the "Lorentz side condition," $\Sigma_j (\partial A_j/\partial x_j) = 0$. (Basically, Maxwell's equations assert that the electromagnetic field is a harmonic 2-form relative to the Minkowski metric; the potentials are the components of a 1-form whose derivative is the field 2-form, and so is ambiguous within an arbitrary additive closed 1-form.) The manifold $\underline{M}$ of all sufficiently regular solutions of these equations--say again of class C^∞ and compact support in space, at any time--together with the group $V(t)$ of temporal translations through t units defined by these differential equations is, apart from one special but important circumstance, uniquely complex Hilbertizable so that the unitary group corresponding to $V(.)$ has positive energy. This circumstance is that the quotient $\underline{L}$ of $\underline{M}$ modulo a subspace of elements of zero norm in the Hilbert space, must be formed; but since such elements of zero norm correspond to closed 1-forms, they contribute nothing to the field strengths, and nothing is lost physically. The resulting system $(\underline{L},V(.))$ (where $V(t)$ is identified with its induced action on the quotient space) then leads to an anti-symmetric positive-energy field as a corollary to the general theory. This procedure is both much simpler and more general than that employed in the theoretical literature; the most popular expedient there, the so-called Gúpta-Bleuler formalism, involves the use of an indefinite metric, and represents a regrettable as well as unnecessary deviation from conventional quantum phenomenological principles.

Some may object that there is a catch to the foregoing procedure: it does not quite determine the quantized electromagnetic field at a point in space-time (or its average relative to a smooth weighting function over a region of space-time); indeed, this is ambiguous, along with the potentials themselves. It is also physically a somewhat mythical object, for a particular free particle associated with this field--the "photon"--is designated not by its position in space (the concept of position in space is somewhat controversial for a relativistic particle; however, in the case of the photon there is general agreement that there is no such thing), but by the corresponding eigenvalues of a complete commuting set of operators (i.e. so-called quantum numbers) derived purely group-theoretically from a set of elements of the enveloping algebra of the Lie algebra of the Poincaré group, which acts irreducibly and unitarily on the completion of $\underline{L}$, relative to the complex Hilbert norm in question. These quantum numbers--energy, momentum, spin, helicity, etc. are relatively quite simple in the indicated formalism.

The one place where the values of the electromagnetic field in space-time appears to be crucially relevant is in the relativistic coupling of the field to other fields. This coupling is defined by relativistic non-linear partial differential equations, which are local in the sense that the terms of the differential equation depend only on the solution in an arbitrarily small neighborhood of one point of space-time; thus the coupled Maxwell-Dirac equations involve products of the form $A_i(x)\Psi_j(x)\overline{\Psi_k(x)}$, where $\Psi_k(.)$ denotes the k-th component of the Dirac field, all multiplied together at the same point. This is mathematically a highly ambiguous object, in the case of quantized fields, and indeed the foundational crux is precisely this point of the actual meaning of this multiplication--a sufficiently serious problem to have given rise to extensive schools of axiomatic, as opposed to constructive, quantum field theory, which abandoned non-linear quantized partial differential equations; and to have persisted from the beginnings of the theory at the hands of Dirac, Rosenfeld, Heisenberg, and Pauli, largely unaltered until quite recently. However, even in a formal sense it is visible that only really physical objects depending on the non-linear term--the so-called interaction hamiltonian--to which I shall come shortly depends only on the field in the modular sense here indicated and indeed is more simply expressed, for actual analytical purposes, in terms of this modular field than any specific representative process in space-time. Roughly speaking the precise localization of the electromagnetic field in space-time is about as plausible but no more necessary than the ether which the Einstein theory eliminated as an objective concept.

The "interaction hamiltonian" and its relation to the "S-operator" are the crux of the dynamical theory of quantum fields. In this hour, I can hardly do more than indicate the basically simple and general but ultimately technically quite sophisticated mathematical problems which are involved here, and the conceptual economy of the physical ideas underlying the theory. The general idea governing the interaction of two free systems is that the interaction should be local, in the sense just indicated, and symmetrical; i.e. invariant under the Poincaré group; in practice this has meant the description of interacting systems by non-linear relativistic (and therefore hyperbolic) partial differential equations. In the case of the Maxwell and Dirac equations, there is a unique simplest symmetrical local coupling, as pointed out very clearly in work years ago by Brauer and Weyl; this is the one which has always been postulated; and since it has led on the one hand to the important physical principle of local conservation of charge, and on the other to notably precise computations explaining quite special observations, such as the Lamb shift measurement, the coupled Maxwell-Dirac equations are closer to being empirically validated than any others of comparable sophistication. The interaction hamiltonian for the coupled quantized Maxwell-Dirac equations is in the first instance the formal expression $\Sigma_{\mu}\int A_{\mu}(\vec{x},t)j_{\mu}(\vec{x},t)d\vec{x}$, where A_{μ} is one of the two unknown (operator-valued, generalized) vector functions and j_{μ} is a bilinear expression in the other vector-valued (actually in this case spinor-valued) functions. The situation is thus somewhat circular: in order to determine A and j, one needs the interaction hamiltonian; but this is defined only in terms of A and j. It is actually worse than this, in that there are presently no applicable general conditions for products or integrals of the indicated sort to exist even as quite singular or generalized operators. One can at this time give a definite meaning to the coupled equations by a generalization applicable to "interacting" fields of the notion of "normal product," whose definition I must forego for lack of time; but the existence theory for such products is still in process of development in the case of free fields. Due to the circularity of the theory, and the singularity of local products of interacting fields, the coupled Maxwell-Dirac equations are presently more readily approached than an equvalent set of equations obtained by the method of the variation of constants, which involve only local products of free fields.

The theoretical physical literature employs the language "Heisenberg field" for an heuristic object which modal usage permits to identify with a solution of the original coupled equations, with suitable boundary conditions; and "interaction-representation" field for another such object which may similarly be identified with the solution of the equations when transformed by a suitable use of the method of variation of constants; in the nature of things, it is not possible mathematically to substantiate this lexicography, which has only the status earlier indicated; but in these terms I shall be "working in the interaction representation."

The method of variation of constants leads formally to a differential equation of the form

$$u' = iH_I(t)u,$$

where the unknown function $u(t)$ has its values in the free field space $\underline{K}$, and $H_I(t)$ is a given expression which formally--but only so--may be identified with a self-adjoint operator on $\underline{K}$; for electrodynamics, $H_I(t)$ has exactly the same expression as before, with the important difference that now the A and the Ψ are free fields. We have thus essentially exchanged the quite nebulous equation

$$v' = i(H_o + H_I)v$$

(or some equivalent equation in purely operational form) by the equation indicated, with $H_I(t) = e^{itH_o} H_I e^{-itH_o}$. This equation is less nebulous in two ways: whereas the Hilbert space in which the values of u lie is unknown, and must be solved for along with the unknown Hilbert space vectors or operators involved in the equation, the space $\underline{K}$ in which v has its values is a given one; second, while the original H_I is defined by a formal expression dependent on unknown functions, the $H_I(t)$ is given by a formal expression involving known functions.

It is therefore logical to begin with the problem of the mathematical meaning (if any) of $H_I(t)$, and of the treatment of such mathematical objects as may emerge from its consideration. This problem has now been solved, in a mathematically quite satisfactory way, in that there is both a very simple intrinsic characterization of $H_I(t)$, and an explicit way to construct it--as yet in a fully detailed way only in the case of scalar fields, although the same methods are applicable to cases like electrodynamics.

The result is , in brief, that $H_I(t)$ is a generalization of the notion of operator in two separate ways. In the first place, it is a closed first-order quantized differential form, in the sense treated in a recent article in Topology in a purely algebraic setting, but here involving certain topological elements. This means roughly that although it is not an operator, its suitably defined commutators with the $A(x,t)$ and $\Psi(x,t)$ behave as if they were commutators with an operator. In the second placc, the coefficients of the form are not operators but generalized operators, i.e. mappings from generalized vectors to generalized vectors; the mappings in question typically carry every non-zero vector in the Hilbert space into a vector outside the Hilbert space. The coefficients may also be regarded as bilinear forms on a dense domain of suitably regular vectors in the Hilbert space--specifically, the physically natural and Lorentz-invariant domain of all infinitely differentiable vectors with respect to the free energy. It is important not only that this formulation is possible, but that it can be done in a way which dovetails with the purpose of integrating the cited differential equation, and conceptually simple mathematical ideas in general, including notably those of locality and the theory of hyperbolic equations. This is necessary for the foundational validation of what would otherwise appear as an ad hoc formulation of doubtful physical relevance.

For example, all of the foregoing theory could just as will be carried out essentially in an arbitrary locally compact abelian group, in place of the euclidean physical space postulated thus far; the renormalized local products at fixed times exist in all such cases under the assumption of the pth power integrability of an associated spectral function on the dual group for large p. On the other hand, in the case of a discrete group there is in addition to the renormalized theory generally available a well-defined naive unrenormalized theory. Which of the two theories--if either--is "physically appropriate?" The notion that this can be decided simply by a straightforward comparison between quantitative predictions and empirical measurements is at best highly oversimplified, particularly in the light of the still unsettled state of the foundations of perturbative renormalization "theory," more than two decades after the "predictions" which were presumed to have validated the theory. For a mathematical-physical development to be well founded, it is not enough to arrive with its use at the correct number or numbers, even after lengthy and arduous considerations; there must also be a basis of scientific (and preferably mathematical) objectivity; to provide such a basis is one of the aims of the work I have described.

Since quantum electrodynamics is a case of unsurpassed mathematical and physical interest, let me return to it and treat finally the determination of its principal empirical manifestation--the S-operator. A classic prescription, poetically (but unfortunately not mathematically) compelling, is that "S is the time-ordered exponential of the interaction Lagrangian" $S = T(e^{i\int \mathcal{L}(\vec{x},t)d\vec{x}\, dt})$. The question of what--if anything--this means in cold prose is equivalent to one of the major--probably <u>the</u> major--foundational problem of the theory. A simple if sophisticated mathematical paraphrase, which is at the same time relatively conservative from a physical standpoint, runs as follows.

First, the "interaction Lagrangian" is a highly idealistic and non-unique notion, and in practice it is usually essentially the same as the interaction Hamiltonian, apart from sign conventions, and the replacement of the integral over space-time by one over space. The Hamiltonian is a more objective and generally applicable notion; in relativistic cases, manifest relativistic invariance is displaced through its use, but this is not a great disadvantage, for the relativistic invariance which can be read off from the Lagrangian is largely formal. As earlier indicated, the interaction hamiltonian $H_I(t)$ is obtainable as a mathematically viable object for suitable fields; it is a highly generalized kind of operator, on a certain Hilbert space <u>K</u>. This leads to a well-defined differential equation for a continuous certain function $u(t,t')$ on $R^1 \times R^1$ to the automorphisms of the appropriately-defined Weyl-Clifford algebra (the Weyl part coming from the Maxwell field, the Clifford part from the Dirac field); $u(t,t')$ is to have the properties

$$u(t,t')u(t',t'') = u(t,t'') \; ; \; u(t,t) = \text{identity},$$

and to satisfy the equation

$$\frac{\partial}{\partial t} u(t,t') = i \, ad(H_I(t))u(t,t')$$

where $ad(Y)$ denotes the suitably defined operation: $X \to [X,Y]$. There are some technical conditions required by virtue of the unboundedness of the operators and similar complications, which cannot be given here. (Incidentally, our physico-mathematical dictionary describes $u(t,t')$ as the transformation taking an observable given at the time t' into the corresponding observable at the time t -- both observables being taken in the frame of reference in which free particles appear stationary.) This is basically simply a first-order ordinary differential equation, although a highly abstract and singular one, whose formulation and solution is a central problem of the theory. The limit of $u(t,t')$ as $t' \to -\infty$ and $t \to \infty$, if it exists in the group of automorphisms of the C*-algebra in question, is the s- (for scattering-) automorphism. There are certain mathematical and physical reasons to anticipate that this limit exists in a number of cases. When it does so, it is evident that s commutes with the one-parameter group of automorphisms induced from the given unitary group earlier denoted as $\Gamma(t)$, and automorphisms induced from the one-parameter group on $\underline{K}$ earlier denoted as $\Gamma(t)$. This implies, by virtue of the uniqueness of positive-energy fields within unitary equivalence, that the automorphism s must be unitarily implementable, via a unitary operator S leaving the (so-called "vacuum") state vector v invariant. By the irreducibility of the free fields, this operator S is unique. Our dictionary describes S as the operator which predicts how a given bunch of free particles which are coming together to interact will probably appear when they have finished doing so; more specifically, if initially the particles are in the state represented by the vector $w \epsilon \underline{K}$, then they will finally be in the state represented by Sw. While this one operator may appear a great deal less than a theoretically complete dynamical description, it appears to determine essentially all that is quantitatively empirical accessible in many cases, including quantum electrodynamics; and there is evidence (in much simpler cases) that the interaction $H_I(t)$ may well be determined, in the presence of natural qualitative assumptions and appropriate regularity hypotheses, by the S-operator.

REFERENCES

The indicated results were largely developed in theses at M.I.T. or the University of Chicago, and/or published in articles referred to in the following surveys which I have made:

1. Mathematical problems of relativistic physics. Providence (Amer. Math. Soc.), 1963.

2. Local non-linear functions of quantum fields. To appear in Proceedings of the Conference in Honor of Marshall H. Stone (Chicago, May, 1968), forthcoming (Springer).

See in particular for some quoted results:

3. M. Weinless, Vacuums of linear quantum fields. To appear in Journal of Functional Analysis.

The basic relevant technical work on non-linear quantum fields includes the following of my papers:

4. Notes towards the construction of non-linear relativistic quantum fields. I. Proc. Nat. Acad. Sci. 57 (1967), 1178-1183.

5. Non-linear functions of weak processes. To appear in Jour. Funct. Anal.

One of the clearest introductions to theoretical physical practice concerning perturbative renormalization theory is:

6. F. Mandl, Introduction to quantum field theory. New York (Interscience), 1959.

Mathematical Problems in the Foundations of Quantum Field Theory

James Glimm*

In the past, connections with physics have been a stimulus to mathematics by providing new problems and by providing new insights into their solutions. It is reasonable to expect that these connections will be rewarding to mathematics in the future also. In the case of quantum field theory, the partial differential equations which specify the time evolution of the system present two novel difficulties. The first difficulty is that the equations contain an infinite number of variables. The second and more serious difficulty is that the equations are exceedingly singular, and usually contain terms having infinite coefficients. In a simple model (the ϕ^4 self-interaction of bosons in two dimensional space time) these difficulties have been overcome, the equations have been given a rigorous mathematical meaning and solutions have been obtained [4,5]. For other models the problem is the same and parti al results have been obtained [2,3]. Basically one wants an existence theorem together with qualitative properties of the solution. The quantitative properties, i.e. accurate numerical calculations, are of even greater fundamental importance since they provide the comparison between theory and experiment. Certainly the existence theory and the numerical problems will appeal to disjoint sets of people, but the two areas are related because the

---

* This paper was written at the Courant Institute of Mathematical Sciences, New York University, under Grant SSF-(8)-8, New York State Science and Technology Foundation.

numerical method of perturbation theory has been adapted in existence problems [2,3]. It is possible that progress with the qualitative properties of solutions may help the numerical calculations by contributing to the judgement as to whether the approximations used in a given calculation are valid. This I believe has been the general experience in the field of partial differential equations. In any case the direct motive for studying existence theory and the qualitative properties of solutions is simply to obtain a deeper understanding of what a quantized field is.

To begin with I will introduce the Hilbert space (called Fock space) used in the two dimensional boson model. It is the direct sum

(1) $$F = \sum \oplus F_n$$

where

(2) $$F_n = SL_2(R^n)$$

is the space of square summable functions of n real variables which are symmetric under permutations of their arguments.

A function

$$\phi_n \in F_n$$

represents a state in which there are exactly n particles, and

$$|\phi_n(k_1,\dots,k_n)|^2$$

is the probability density that their momenta be $k_1,\dots,k_n$. If the particles did not interact then their motion would be governed by the Klein-Gordon equation, or rather by the positive energy factor

(3) $$i\frac{\partial}{\partial t} - \sqrt{-\Delta + m^2}$$

of the Klein-Gordon operator

(4) $$\Box + m^2 = \left(i\frac{\partial}{\partial t} - \sqrt{-\Delta+m^2}\right)\left(i\frac{\partial}{\partial t} + \sqrt{-\Delta+m^2}\right) .$$

Since we are working in momentum, or Fourier Transform space, and since each particle has a motion governed by (3), we see that the dynamics in the absence of interaction is given by

$$(5)\quad \begin{cases} \phi_n(t,k_1,\ldots,k_n) = e^{-itH_0}\,\phi(0,k_1,\ldots,k_n) \\ H_0\phi_n(k_1,\ldots,k_n) = \sum_{j=1}^{n} \mu(k_j)\,\phi_n(k_1,\ldots,k_n) \\ \mu(k) = \sqrt{k^2+m^2}. \end{cases}$$

H_0 is called the free Hamiltonian operator. The total Hamiltonian operator has the form

$$H = H_0 + H_I$$

where H_I gives the energy of the interaction. To describe H_I, we first represent it in terms of diagrams,

(6) $H_I =$  .

We now explain the meaning of the symbols above.

Consider as a typical term,

.

This term is an operator which annihilates one boson and subsequently creates three bosons. Thus

: $F_n \to F_{n+2}$.

To define this operator more exactly, we are given by the physics a kernel v (a distribution in four variables) and we have

$$(7)\qquad (\ni \phi_n)(k_1,\ldots,k_{n+2})$$

$$= (n+2)^{1/2}(n+1)^{1/2} n\, S \int v(k_n, k_{n+1}, k_{n+2}, k)$$

$$\times\, \phi_n(k_1,\ldots,k_{n-1},k)\ dk\ .$$

To be precise,

$$(8)\qquad v = \binom{4}{1}\, \delta(k_1+k_2+k_3-k_4) \prod_{j=1}^{4} \mu(k_j)^{-1/2}\ .$$

S is the symmetrization projection. Analogously

$$(9)\qquad (\ni \phi_n)(k_1,\ldots,k_{n+4})$$

$$= (n+4)^{1/2} \ldots (n+1)^{1/2}\, S\, w(k_{n+1},\ldots,k_{n+4})\ \phi_n(k_1,\ldots,k_n)$$

$$(10)\qquad w = \binom{4}{0}\, \delta(k_1+\ldots+k_4) \prod_{j=1}^{4} \mu(k_j)^{-1/2}\ .$$

The singularity of this term is evident because $w \notin L_2$ and $\ni \phi_n \notin F$ unless $\phi_n = 0$. Clearly the delta function causes the trouble and one can trace the difficulty back to basic physical principles and discover that the δ function arises because particles can interact with uniform strength anywhere in the infinite volume of space. A mathematical derivation uses the fact that δ is the Fourier transform of the function 1. This singularity is called a volume singularity. In higher dimensions there are other and more serious singularities caused by the slow decrease of the kernels v and w at infinity. The latter singularity gives rise to the well known ultraviolet divergences of quantum field theory. These singularities give rise to a shift -- by an infinite amount -- in the spectrum of H (as compared to the spectrum of H_0) and to recover the finite spectral values observed by experiment, we introduce new terms into the Hamiltonian, writing

(11) $$H_{ren} = H_0 + H_I + C$$

Here C is a counter term, and is a sum of operators multiplied by infinite coefficients. In physical terms, C is described easily as the effect of changing a few parameters in the theory (mass, vacuum energy, charge) but the change is by an infinite amount. In mathematical terms, the role of C is to compensate for and cancel infinite quantities arising from products of H_0 and H_I. The central mathematical problem is then to make sense out of the dynamics governed by the singular energy operator (11), either by giving a meaning to (11) directly or by reformulating the dynamics so that (11) does not occur.

To give a meaning to (11) and to perform the infinite cancellations rigorously, we introduce as a first step approximations in (11). In the approximate, cutoff or regularized version of (11), the kernels v, w,... in H_I are replaced by smooth functions, for example by the substitution

$$\delta = 1\hat{} \to \hat{g}$$

where g is a C^∞ function with compact support, equal to one on a large bounded set. The operator H_I can be written as the integral of a density,

$$H_I = \int H_I(x)\, dx.$$

and the above substitution gives us

$$H_I(g) = \int H_I(x)\, g(x)\, dx.$$

As a result of this cutoff, the counter term C becomes finite. We set

(12) $$H(g) = H_0 + H_I(g) - E_g I$$

(13) $$E_g = \inf \text{spectrum} \{ H_0 + H_I(g) \}$$

For higher dimensions, a momentum cutoff is also required in order that all counter terms become finite.

The second step is to study the theory constructed with the approximate or $H(g)$-dynamics, and especially to obtain estimates which are uniform in g. These estimates are the crucial point and to succeed they must somehow reflect the fact that in the approximate theory large but finite cancellations occur. The final step is to pass to the limit $g \to 1$. Essentially these steps were proposed by Wightman in 1964 [7].

The main results for $H(g)$ for the ϕ^4 interaction in two dimensional space time can be summarized as follows [1, 4, 5, 6].

Theorem 1.

a) E_g is finite and so $H(g)$ is defined by (12);

b) $H(g)$ is a positive self-adjoint operator;

c) zero is an eigenvalue of $H(g)$ with multiplicity 1.

We use $H(g)$ to define the Heisenberg picture field operators

$$\phi(x,t) = e^{itH(g)} \phi(x) e^{-itH(g)}$$

and

$$\phi(f) = \int \phi(x,t) f(x,t) \, dx \, dt,$$

where the Cauchy data $\phi(x)$ is the free field at time zero. Because influence propagates at a finite speed in the Heisenberg picture, $\phi(x,t)$ is independent of g provided $g(y) = 1$ whenever

$$|x - y| \leq |t| \quad ,$$

see [4,5] and the references cited there.

Theorem 2.

a) $\phi(x,t)$ is an unbounded bilinear form depending continuously on x and t;

b) $\phi(f)$ is self-adjoint for real test functions f;

c) $\phi(f)$ depends continuously on f;

d) $\phi(x,t)$ satisfies the Heisenberg equations of motion;

e) $\phi(x,t)$ is covariant under space-time translations;

f) ϕ is local, i.e. $\phi(f_1)$ and $\phi(f_2)$ commute if the supports of f_1 and f_2 are spacelike separated.

The proof of this theorem will be given in [5]; this paper will also deal with the problem of obtaining the physical vacuum as a limit of the H(g) vacua Ω_g:

$$H(g)\ \Omega_g = 0$$

and with the problem of obtaining H_{ren} in (11) as a limit of the H(g).

The proof of Theorems 1 and 2 rests upon estimates, that is on inequalities between operators. To illustrate this, we indicate the proof of self adjointness of H(g), assuming the estimates

(14) $$H_0^2 + H_I(g)^2 \leq \text{const.}\ (H(g) + \text{const.})^2$$

(15) $$\|(H_0 + I)^{-1}\ H_I(g)\ (H_0 + I)^{-1}\| \leq \text{const.}$$

We introduce a further approximation $H_I(g,n)$ chosen so that

$$H_I(g) \doteq \lim H_I(g,n)$$

$$||(H_0 + I)^{-1}[H_I(g,n) - H_I(g,m)] \ (H_0 + I)^{-1}|| \ \to \ 0.$$

We further require that

$$H_n = H_0 + H_I(g,n)$$

be self-adjoint and that the estimate (14) hold for $H_I(g,n)$ with constants independent of n. Then setting

$$R_n(z) = (H_n - z)^{-1}$$

we have

$$R_n(z) - R_m(z) = R_n(g)[H_I(g,n) - H_I(g,m)]R_m(z) \quad ,$$

$$||R_n(z) - R_m(z)|| \leq ||R_n(z)(H_0+I)|| \ \ ||(H_0+I)R_m(z)||$$

$$\times ||(H_0+I)^{-1}[H_I(g,n) - H_I(g,m)](H_0+I)^{-1}|| .$$

Using (14) for H_m, we have

$$||(H_0+I)R_m(z)|| \leq \text{const.} \ \ ||(H_m + \text{const.})R_m(z)||$$

$$\leq \text{const.}$$

$$||R_n(z)(H_0+I)|| = ||(H_0+I)R_n(z)^*|| \leq \text{const.}$$

Thus the resolvents converge uniformly and the self-adjointness of H(g) follows from this.

The limit H = lim H(g) requires the theory of operator algebras, the reason being that the limit does not exist in any conventional sense of strong limits of operators in Hilbert space. In fact calculations in perturbation theory indicate that the ground state Ω_g of H(g) converges weakly to zero as $g \to 1$. These calculations also show that in the limit $g \to 1$, one can regard Ω_g as leaving the original Hilbert space F and converging to an element of a new Hilbert space. To handle this type of limit mathematically, we form a C^*-algebra $\mathfrak{A}$ from bounded functions of the field operators $\phi(f)$. Instead of seeking a limit of the vectors Ω_g, we find a limit point ω of the linear functionals $\omega_g \in \mathfrak{A}^*$:

$$\omega_g(A) = (\Omega_g, A\Omega_g) , \qquad A \in \mathfrak{A} .$$

By the Gelfand Segal construction, there is a new Hilbert space F', a vector $\Omega \in F'$ and a representation π of $\mathfrak{A}$ ~~as~~ operators on F' such that

$$\omega(A) = (\Omega, \pi(A)\, \Omega) .$$

The existence of ω follows from the w* compactness of the dual space $\mathfrak{A}^*$, but the derivation of important properties of ω will apparently require good estimates on the approximate vacua ω_g and on their convergence to ω. There is no difficulty in showing that

$$(A\Omega_g, e^{-itH(g)} B\Omega_g) \to (\pi(A)\Omega, U(t)\, \pi(B)\Omega)$$

where U(t) is a uniquely determined unitary operator on F'. These U's form a continuous one parameter group. If H is the generator, then

$$U(t) = e^{-itH}$$

and H is a positive self adjoint operator. We regard H as the limit of the H(g) and as the mathematically rigorous description of the formal operator (11). Certainly the limiting procedure used to define H should be investigated in more detail and in a more general setting.

References

1. Glimm, J., Boson fields with nonlinear selfinteraction in two dimensions. Comm. Math. Phys. 8, 12-25 (1968).

2. __________, The foundations of quantum field theory. Advances in Math., to appear.

3. __________, Models for quantum field theory. Italian summer school of theoretical physics, Varenna, Italy.

4. __________, and A. Jaffe, A $(\phi^4)_2$ quantum field theory without cutoffs, I. Phys. Rev., to appear.

5. ______________________, A $(\phi^4)_2$ quantum field theory without cutoffs, II. To appear.

6. Nelson, E., A quartic interaction in two dimensions. In: Mathematical theory of elementary particles. ed. by R. Goodman and I. Segal, pp. 69-73, M.I.T. Press, 1965.

7. Wightman, A., An introduction to some aspects of the relativistic dynamics of quantized fields. In 1964 Cargèse Summer School lectures, M. Levy, editor. Gordon and Breach, New York, 1967.

NEW METHODS AND PROBLEMS

IN STATISTICAL MECHANICS

D. Ruelle

I.H.E.S.

91 - Bures-sur-Yvette. France.

Abstract. Recent developments in the statistical mechanics of infinite systems are discussed. Some insight into the meaning of the Gibbs phase rule is obtained.

0. Introduction. The Gibbs phase rule.

The history of mathematical physics in recent years has consisted largely in trying to understand the structure of physical systems with an infinite number of degrees of freedom. A relatively tractable example of such systems is provided by statistical mechanics. In this lecture I shall describe some of the results which have been obtained in the statistical mechanics of infinite systems.

To be definite, I shall set myself the aim of trying to explain the Gibbs phase rule of thermodynamics from the basic principles of statistical mechanics. In doing so I shall have the opportunity of reviewing a certain number of the methods and problems which have arisen in statistical mechanics during the last few years.

Let me now remind you briefly of the Gibbs phase rule. Consider a one-component thermodynamic system like water. For given values of two independent thermodynamic variables an equilibrium state should (in general) be defined. More precisely, the Gibbs phase rule tells us that in the plane of two intensive thermodynamic parameters almost all points correspond to a pure thermodynamic phase, that there are curves * of coexistence of two phases and isolated points of coexistence of three phases. For instance, using the variables p, T, the familiar phase diagram is obtained.

---

*) To be precise one should assert certain smoothness properties of these curves.

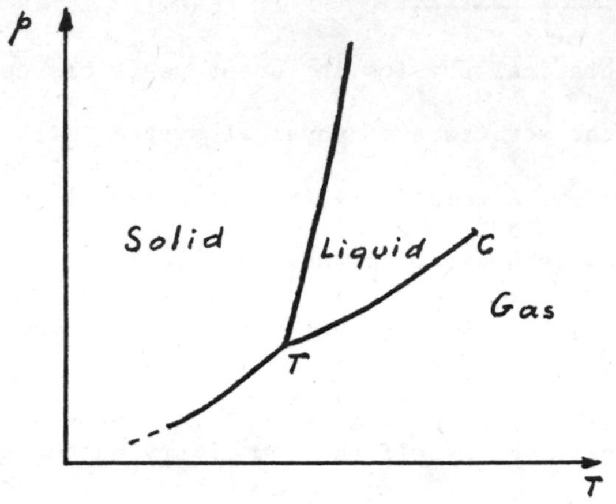

To prove a strong version of the Gibbs phase rule is tantamount of making a theory of phase transitions and is beyond what can be done for the moment. I shall here concern myself with a weak phase rule saying essentially that the set of points in the (p,T) diagram which do not correspond to a pure thermodynamic phase is "small" at least "for most interactions". These concepts and also what is meant by a "pure thermodynamic phase" will have to be precised.

The present report is based upon work by Gallavotti, Miracle ([1],[2]), Lanford, Robinson and Ruelle ([3]-[8]) . A more detailed treatment of the subject can be found in a series of lectures "On the Gibbs Phase Rule" given in Noordwyk (The Netherlands) in 1967 (published by North Holland, 1968) ; see also a forthcoming book "Statistical Mechanics, Rigorous results" to be published by Benjamin in 1969.

In order to avoid certain complications and technical difficulties I shall restrict myself to a very simple class of systems called lattice gases. The logical structure of the discussion is outlined in the following diagram.

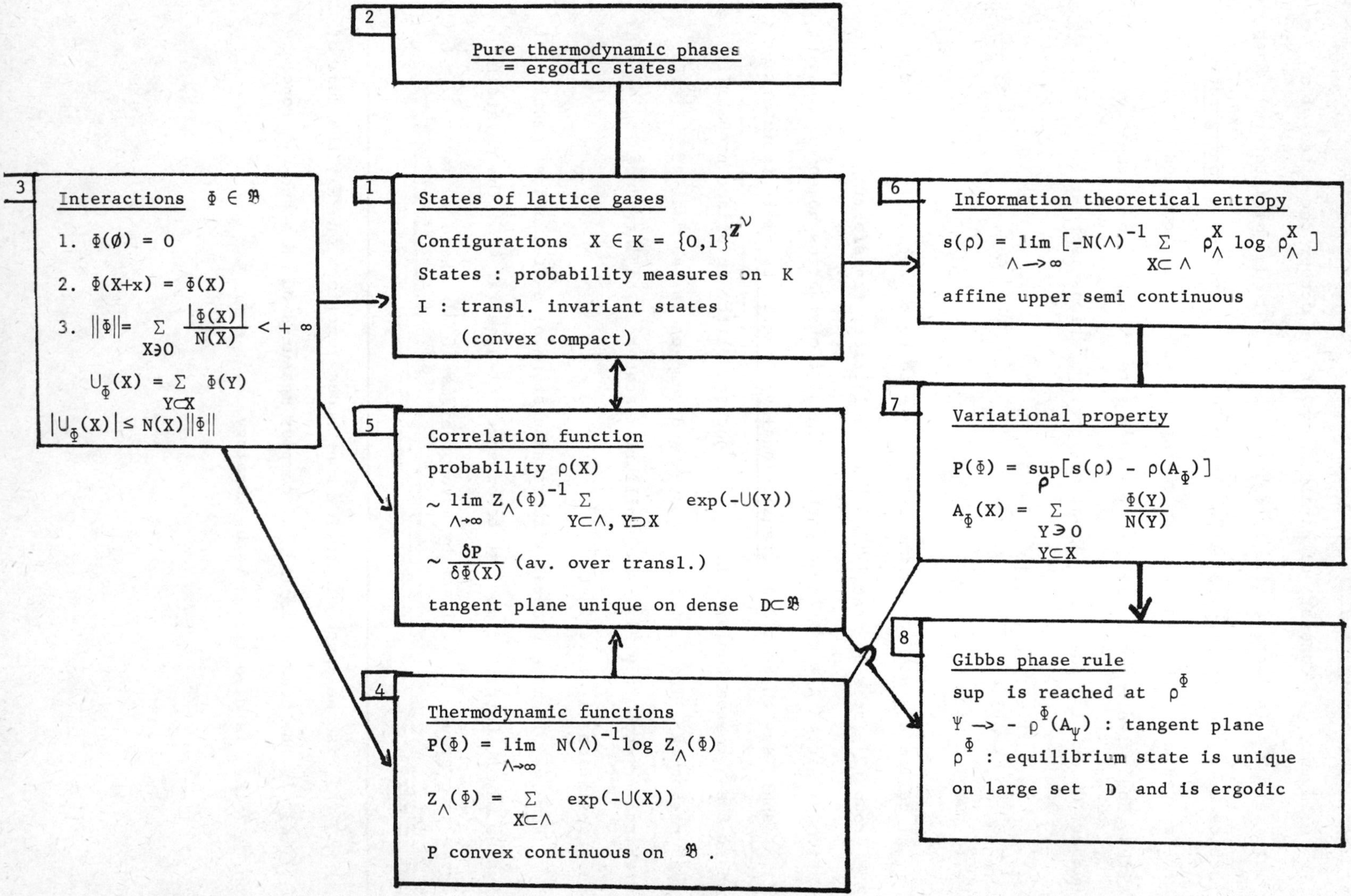
2 Pure thermodynamic phases = ergodic states
3 Interactions $\Phi \in \mathfrak{B}$
1. $\Phi(\emptyset) = 0$
2. $\Phi(X+x) = \Phi(X)$
3. $\|\Phi\| = \sum_{X \ni 0} \frac{|\Phi(X)|}{N(X)} < +\infty$
$U_\Phi(X) = \sum_{Y \subset X} \Phi(Y)$
$|U_\Phi(X)| \le N(X)\|\Phi\|$
1 States of lattice gases
Configurations $X \in K = \{0,1\}^{\mathbf{Z}^\nu}$
States : probability measures on K
I : transl. invariant states
(convex compact)
6 Information theoretical entropy
$s(\rho) = \lim_{\Lambda \to \infty} [-N(\Lambda)^{-1} \sum_{X \subset \Lambda} \rho_\Lambda^X \log \rho_\Lambda^X]$
affine upper semi continuous
5 Correlation function
probability $\rho(X)$
$\sim \lim_{\Lambda\to\infty} Z_\Lambda(\Phi)^{-1} \sum_{Y\subset\Lambda,\, Y\supset X} \exp(-U(Y))$
$\sim \frac{\delta P}{\delta\Phi(X)}$ (av. over transl.)
tangent plane unique on dense $D \subset \mathfrak{B}$
7 Variational property
$P(\Phi) = \sup_\rho [s(\rho) - \rho(A_\Phi)]$
$A_\Phi(X) = \sum_{Y \ni 0,\, Y \subset X} \frac{\Phi(Y)}{N(Y)}$
4 Thermodynamic functions
$P(\Phi) = \lim_{\Lambda\to\infty} N(\Lambda)^{-1} \log Z_\Lambda(\Phi)$
$Z_\Lambda(\Phi) = \sum_{X\subset\Lambda} \exp(-U(X))$
P convex continuous on $\mathfrak{B}$.
8 Gibbs phase rule
sup is reached at ρ^Φ
$\Psi \to -\rho^\Phi(A_\Psi)$: tangent plane
ρ^Φ : equilibrium state is unique
on large set D and is ergodic

1. States of lattice gases.

A lattice gas consists of particles which can occupy the sites of a "lattice" $\mathbb{Z}^\nu$ (a lattice site is labelled by a ν-tuple of integers). Each lattice site can be occupied either by 0 or 1 particle. A configuration of the system is thus described by giving the set X of occupied lattice sites. Equivalently one may give for each site $x \in \mathbb{Z}^\nu$ the occupation number 0 or 1 ; the space K of all configurations is then

$$K = \{0,1\}^{\mathbb{Z}^\nu}$$

K is compact with the product topology.

I define a state ρ of the lattice gas to be a probability measure on K . The group $\mathbb{Z}^\nu$ acts by translations of the lattice, transforming the configuration X into $X + x$. These lattice translations define homeomorphisms of K . I shall say that ρ is (translationally) invariant if it is invariant under these homeomorphisms. Let I be the set of the invariant probability measures on K . The set I is convex and compact in the dual of $\mathcal{C}(K)$ with the w*-topology *) . The equilibrium states to be introduced below will be translationally invariant.

Remark. In more general situations a state of a statistical mechanical system may be described by a state on some C*-algebra $\mathcal{A}$. The physical invariance group G will act by automorphisms of $\mathcal{A}$. Here we have $\mathcal{A} = \mathcal{C}(K)$ and $G = \mathbb{Z}^\nu$.

) $\mathcal{C}(K)$ is the space of complex continuous functions on K ; the dual of $\mathcal{C}(K)$ is the space $\mathcal{M}(K)$ of complex measures on K ; the w-topology on $\mathcal{M}(K)$ is also called vague topology.

2. Pure Thermodynamic phases.

The extremal points of the set I of invariant states are the ergodic states. I want to argue that a state ρ with the physical interpretation of an equilibrium state will describe a pure thermodynamic phase if and only if it is ergodic.

Let me first introduce the point of view that the elements A of $\mathcal{C}(K)$, viz. the continuous functions on K, can be interpreted as observable quantities. If ρ is a state, $\rho(A)$ will be the expectation value of A in the state ρ. In particular if Λ is a finite subset of $\mathbb{Z}^{\nu}$ and if the function $X \longrightarrow A(X)$ depends on X only through $X \cap \Lambda$, A will describe what happens in Λ (A is then called a local observable, the local observables are dense in $\mathcal{C}(K)$ by Stone-Weierstrass). It is possible to express in the form $\rho(A)$ things like the probability that a certain number of lattice points be simultaneously occupied and some others empty. If A is self-adjoint, a state ρ determines in a natural manner a probability measure on the spectrum of A; in general this measure is not concentrated on a point of the spectrum and we say that the observable A fluctuates.

Define the average $< A >_n \in \mathcal{C}(K)$ of A over translations in a cube with side n :

$$< A >_n = n^{-\nu} \sum_{x^1=1}^{n} \cdots \sum_{x^{\nu}=1}^{n} \tau_x A$$

where

$$\tau_x A(X) = A(X - x) \quad .$$

It follows from the mean ergodic theorem that (for $\rho \in I$) ρ is ergodic if and only if, for all self-adjoint $A \in \mathcal{C}(K)$,

$$\lim_{n \to \infty} \rho([< A >_n]^2) = [\rho(A)]^2 \quad .$$

Using $\rho(< A >_n) = \rho(A)$, this can also be written

$$\lim_{n \to \infty} \rho([< A >_n - \rho(A)]^2) = 0 \quad . \tag{1}$$

We know that the observables A and $< A >_n$ fluctuate in general in the state ρ ; (1) says that, for large n , $< A >_n$ fluctuates very little. It is natural to say that ρ corresponds to a pure thermodynamic phase when (*) holds for all A , i.e. when space-averaged or "coarse-grained" quantities $< A >_n$ reduce to constants (for large n). If (*) does not hold, some coarse-grained quantities (like the mean number of particles per site) fluctuate and we have a mixture.

Remark. Every invariant state ρ may be considered as a mixture and has an integral representation in terms of ergodic states. Using Choquet's theory of integral representations on convex compact sets one can extend this result to a large class of C*- algebras with groups of automorphisms.

3. Interactions.

In order to define equilibrium states I have to introduce an interaction between particles. It will be convenient for the purposes of this talk to define an interaction as a real function $\Phi : X \longrightarrow \Phi(X)$ on the finite subsets of $\mathbb{Z}^{\nu}$, where the following conditions have to be satisfied

1. $\Phi(\emptyset) = 0$.
2. Translational invariance : $\Phi(X+x) = \Phi(X)$.
3. $$\|\Phi\| = \sum_{X \ni 0} \frac{|\Phi(X)|}{N(X)} < +\infty .$$

where $N(X)$ denotes the number of points in X . The interactions form thus a real Banach space $\mathfrak{B}$ with respect to the norm $\|.\|$.

If a finite set $X \subset \mathbb{Z}^{\nu}$ of lattice sites are occupied by particles, the energy of these particles with respect to the interaction *) Φ is defined to be

$$U_{\Phi}(X) = \sum_{Y \subset X} \Phi(Y) .$$

Clearly $U_{\Phi}(X+x) = U_{\Phi}(X)$. The norm $\|.\|$ in $\mathfrak{B}$ is such that

$$| U_{\Phi}(X) | \leq N(X) \|\Phi\|$$

i.e. the energy of N particles is bounded in absolute value by a multiple of N .

Now that the energy has been defined it is possible to write the usual formulas of statistical mechanics.

---

*) If $\Phi(X)$ vanishes for $N(X) > 2$ one would call Φ a pair interaction and $\Phi(\{x,y\})$ the pair potential between x and y .

4. Thermodynamic functions.

A priori it appears that equilibrium statistical mechanics should be mainly concerned with equilibrium states. In fact the study of equilibrium states is invariably preceeded by the study of thermodynamic functions. I shall follow the rule, defining now the thermodynamic function P and discussing later what its relation to equilibrium states is.

Theorem. For finite $\Lambda \subset \mathbb{Z}^{\nu}$, let *)

$$Z_{\Lambda}(\Phi) = \sum_{X \subset \Lambda} \exp[-U_{\Phi}(X)]$$

$$P_{\Lambda}(\Phi) = N(\Lambda)^{-1} \log Z_{\Lambda}(\Phi) .$$

If Λ is a parallelepiped with sides tending to ∞ **), the following limit exists

$$P(\Phi) = \lim_{\Lambda \to \infty} P_{\Lambda}(\Phi)$$

and is a convex continuous function of Φ on the Banach space $\mathfrak{B}$.

The function P (of the interaction) is a "thermodynamic function" which can be interpreted as "pressure" of our lattice gas. Usually, the pressure is exhibited as a function of the chemical potential μ and the inverse temperature β ; one writes

$$\beta\, p(\mu,\beta) = \lim_{\Lambda \to \infty} N(\Lambda)^{-1} \log \sum_{X \subset \Lambda} \exp[\beta\mu\, N(X) - \beta\, U_{\Phi'}(X)]$$

where it is assumed that $\Phi'(X) = 0$ when $N(X) = 1$. Clearly μ can be absorbed in the definition of the interaction by letting $\Phi'(X) = -\mu$ when

---

*) Z_{Λ} is called the "grand partition function" of the region Λ .

**) One may actually let Λ tend to infinity in a much more general manner.

$N(X) = 1$. Similarly β is just a multiplicative factor which may be absorbed in the definition of the interaction by letting $\Phi = \beta\, \Phi'$.

Let me come back to my ultimate aim which is to prove that an equilibrium state is "in general" a pure thermodynamic phase. In this statement the phrase "in general" will mean : for most interactions Φ , where Φ contains the intensive thermodynamic variables μ , β as we just saw.

Remark. The limit of an infinite system, obtained by letting Λ tend to infinity, is called "thermodynamic limit". The theorem quoted above establishes the existence of the thermodynamic limit of the thermodynamic function P.

The fact that we are dealing with lattice systems simplifies considerably the discussion of the thermodynamic limit. For a continuous system of particles, interacting through a pair potential φ , very restrictive conditions have to be imposed upon φ to ensure that the system will have a thermodynamic behavior. For instance if φ is a "good" pair potential, - φ is generally bad.

5. Correlation function.

I have defined a state of a lattice gas as a probability measure ρ on the set $K = \{0,1\}^{\mathbb{Z}^\nu}$ of the configurations of the system. It is convenient to describe ρ by its correlation function *) $\rho : X \longrightarrow \rho(X)$. This function is defined on the finite subsets of $\mathbb{Z}^\nu$ and $\rho(X)$ has to be interpreted as the probability that all points of X are occupied by a particle irrespective of what may happen in the complement of X . It can be checked that the correlation function completely specifies the state.

The standard formula giving the correlation function of the equilibrium state for the interaction Φ is according to textbooks

$$\rho(X) = \lim_{\Lambda \to \infty} Z(\Lambda)^{-1} \sum_{\substack{Y \subset \Lambda \\ Y \supset X}} \exp(-U(Y)) \qquad . \tag{2}$$

The existence of this limit can however not be established in general. There arises thus the problem of how to define an equilibrium state. A reasonable answer to the problem is as follows. First, take the average over translations (in $\mathbb{Z}^\nu$) of the expression in the right-hand side of (2) **) . Second, take any limit of the resulting expression when Λ tends to infinity in a suitable manner ***) , this is by definition the correlation function of some

---

*) The same letter ρ is here used to denote a state and the corresponding correlation function.

**) We define this average to be $N(\Lambda)^{-1} \sum_{x \,:\, x+X \subset \Lambda} [Z(\Lambda)^{-1} \sum_{\substack{Y \subset \Lambda \\ Y \supset x+X}} \exp(-U(Y))]$

$= N(\Lambda)^{-1} Z(\Lambda)^{-1} \sum_{Y \subset \Lambda} \exp(-U(Y)) \, [\sum_{x \,:\, x+X \subset Y} 1 \,]$

***) For instance a parallelepiped with sides tending to infinity.

equilibrium state for the interaction Φ .

Coming back to the average over translations of the expression in the right-hand side of (2), one can check immediately that it is the functional derivative

$$- \frac{\delta P_{\Lambda}}{\delta \Phi(X)} .$$

Since $P_{\Lambda} \longrightarrow P$ when $\Lambda \longrightarrow \infty$ one verifies that the correlation function of an equilibrium state corresponds to a tangent plane to the graph of the (convex) function $\Phi \longrightarrow P(\Phi)$.

An interesting situation arises when this tangent plane is unique, because the equilibrium state is then uniquely determined. Let $D \subset \mathfrak{B}$ be the set of interactions for which the equilibrium state is thus uniquely defined. One can show that D is a "large" set , in particular it contains a countable intersection of dense open subsets of $\mathfrak{B}$ and is therefore dense in $\mathfrak{B}$ by Baire. To summarize : <u>there is a large set</u> D <u>of interactions</u> Φ <u>for which the equilibrium state is well defined</u>, <u>the correlation function of this equilibrium state corresponds to the</u> (<u>unique</u>) <u>tangent plane to the graph of</u> P <u>over</u> Φ .

6. Information theoretical entropy.

Given a state ρ , a finite set $\Lambda \subset \mathbf{Z}^{\nu}$, and $X \subset \Lambda$, let me denote by ρ_{Λ}^{X} the probability that the points of X are occupied by a particle and the points of $\Lambda \backslash X$ empty. A mean entropy $s(\rho)$ is associated with the invariant state ρ by

$$s(\rho) = \lim_{\Lambda \to \infty} N(\Lambda)^{-1} S(\Lambda) = \inf_{\Lambda} N(\Lambda)^{-1} S(\Lambda)$$

where the entropy $S(\Lambda)$ of Λ is defined by

$$S(\Lambda) = - \sum_{X \subset \Lambda} \rho_{\Lambda}^{X} \log \rho_{\Lambda}^{X}$$

and Λ runs over parallelepipeds as usual *) .

Theorem. The functional $s(.)$ is affine upper semi-continuous on the convex compact set I of invariant states.

The upper semicontinuity follows from the fact that $s(.)$ is a lower bound of continuous functions. By mixing two states : ρ_1 , $\rho_2 \longrightarrow \rho = \alpha\rho_1 + (1-\alpha)\rho_2$ one obtains a state with entropy $S(\Lambda) > \alpha S_1(\Lambda) + (1-\alpha) S_2(\Lambda)$, i.e. $S(\Lambda)$ is larger than the average of the entropies of Λ for ρ_1 and ρ_2 , but not by more than log 2 ; from this the affine character of $s(.)$ follows immediately.

Remark. The mean entropy introduced above is a ν-dimensional extension of the entropy of information theory defined for $\nu = 1$. The connexion consists in that a one-dimensional lattice gas is viewed by information theorists as a message written in binary alphabet (with letters 0, 1).

---

*) The fact that $\lim_{\Lambda \to \infty}$ exists and is equal to $\inf_{\Lambda}$ comes from the fact that the entropy $S(\Lambda)$ is a subadditive function of each side of the parallelepiped Λ .

7. Variational property.

Having introduced the mean entropy of an invariant state it is natural to investigate if the mean entropy of an equilibrium state has anything to do with its thermodynamic entropy. It turns out in fact that the two concepts coincide.

According to accepted ideas, the (equilibrium) thermodynamic entropy corresponding to given values of the density and mean energy is the supremum of the entropies of those states which have the right density and energy. One can take into account the restrictions to fixed density and mean energy by using Lagrange multipliers. From the usual machinery of thermodynamic formulas one expects then the variational principle

$$P(\Phi) = \sup_{\rho \in I} [s(\rho) - \rho(A_\Phi)] \qquad (3)$$

where $\rho(A_\Phi)$ is the expectation value in the state ρ of the energy per site for the interaction Φ (in view of our conventions this contains also a chemical potential times density term and an inverse temperature factor). The element A_Φ of $\mathcal{C}(K)$ is an "observable quantity" namely the contribution of the site 0 of the lattice to the energy ; it is defined by

$$A_\Phi(X) = \sum_{Y \ni 0 \ , \ Y \subset X} \frac{\Phi(Y)}{N(Y)} \ .$$

Let me conclude this section by saying that the variational formula (3) can be proved from the definitions given above. This shows in particular that $s(\rho)$ is the thermodynamic entropy. I shall now use (3) to prove the announced weak version of the Gibbs phase rule.

8. The Gibbs phase rule.

The supremum in the variational formula (3) is actually reached because the expression in square brackets is upper semi-continuous on the compact set I . Let ρ^{Φ} be one of the invariant states such that

$$P(\Phi) = s(\rho^{\Phi}) - \rho^{\Phi}(A_{\Phi}) \quad .$$

It is natural to think that ρ^{Φ} is an equilibrium state for the interaction Φ . Let me show that this is indeed the case, in the sense that ρ^{Φ} corresponds to a tangent plane to the graph of $P(.)$. For any $\Psi \in \mathfrak{B}$ we have

$$\begin{aligned} P(\Phi+\Psi) &= \sup_{\rho}(s(\rho) - \rho(A_{\Phi+\Psi})) \\ &\geq s(\rho^{\Phi}) - \rho^{\Phi}(A_{\Phi}) - \rho^{\Phi}(A_{\Psi}) \\ &= P(\Phi) - \rho^{\Phi}(A_{\Psi}) \end{aligned}$$

and therefore the linear functional $\Psi \longrightarrow - \rho^{\Phi}(A_{\Psi})$ defines a tangent plane to the graph of $P(.)$.

Let now $\Phi \in D$, i.e. let there be a unique tangent plane to the graph of $P(.)$, then one can check that ρ^{Φ} is exactly the equilibrium state as defined in section 5. Furthermore ρ^{Φ} is then the only invariant state which maximizes $s(\rho) - \rho(A_{\Phi})$. But since $s(\rho)$ is affine and I convex, this unique maximum can occur only at an extremal point of I , namely at an ergodic state. Finally, an ergodic state may be interpreted as a pure thermodynamic phase as we argued in Section 2. We have thus established the desired weak form of the Gibbs phase rule : <u>if the interaction</u> Φ <u>belongs to the large set</u> $D \subset \mathfrak{B}$, <u>then the (unique) equilibrium state</u> ρ^{Φ} <u>describes a pure thermodynamic phase</u>.

BIBLIOGRAPHY.

[1] Gallavotti G. and Miracle-Sole S. Statistical Mechanics of Lattice Systems. Commun. Math. Phys. 5, 317-323 (1967).

[2] Gallavotti G. and Miracle-Sole S. A Variational Principle for the Equilibrium of Hard Sphere Systems. Ann. Inst. Henri Poincaré 8, 287-299 (1968).

[3] Lanford O. and Robinson D.W. Mean Entropy of States in Quantum Statistical Mechanics. J. Math. Phys. 9, 1120-1125 (1968).

[4] Lanford O. and Robinson D. W. Statistical Mechanics of Quantum Spin Systems. III. Commun. Math. Phys. 9, 327-338 (1968).

[5] Robinson D. W. Statistical Mechanics of Quantum Spin Systems. I. Commun. Math. Phys. 6, 151-160 (1967). II. Commun. Math. Phys. 7, 337-348 (1968).

[6] Robinson D. W. and Ruelle D. Mean Entropy of States in Classical Statistical Mechanics. Commun. Math. Phys. 5, 288-300 (1967).

[7] Ruelle D. A Variational Formulation of Equilibrium Statistical Mechanics and the Gibbs Phase Rule. Commun. Math. Phys. 5, 324-329 (1967).

[8] Ruelle D. Some Remarks on the Ground State of Infinite Systems in Statistical Mechanics. Commun. Math. Phys. To appear.

Abstract Wiener Measure and Infinite Dimensional Potential Theory

by

Leonard Gross

INTRODUCTION. Our aim in this paper is firstly to develop in detail the theory of abstract Wiener measure and secondly to describe in a brief survey form some of its applications to analysis over infinite dimensional spaces. In sections one and two of this paper we shall define and establish the countable additivity of abstract Wiener measure. This part of the paper is fairly self contained.

In section three we shall describe the present state of progress in infinite dimensional potential theory. Consider for the moment the equation

1) $$\frac{1}{2}\Delta u = -g$$

where u and g are functions on R^n and

2) $$\Delta u = \sum_{j=1}^{n} \frac{\partial^2 u}{\partial x_j^2} .$$

An important solution to this equation is the potential of g, namely

3) $$u(x) = \int_{R^n} g(x-y)\, F(dy)$$

where F is the fundamental solution which we regard here as a measure on R^n. Thus

4) $$F(A) = \frac{1}{(n-2)\omega_n} \int_A \frac{1}{|x|^{n-2}} \, dx$$

where $|x|$ is the Euclidean length of x, A is a Borel set in R^n and ω_n is the surface area of the unit sphere in R^n.

We wish to give meaning to equations 1) - 4) when $n = \infty$. In equation 4) however, three difficulties become apparent as $n \to \infty$. Firstly the constant $((n-2)\omega_n)^{-1}$ approaches zero as $n \to \infty$. Secondly the integrand $|x|^{2-n}$ approaches a function taking only the values 0, 1, and ∞. And thirdly the Lebesgue measure dx on R^n becomes completely meaningless.

It is therefore particularly edifying that the measure $F(A)$ can nevertheless be given a meaning when $n = \infty$ in such a way that equations 1) - 3) remain valid. Indeed the measure F can be written (for n finite) in the form

5) $$F(A) = \int_0^\infty p_t(A) \, dt$$

where p_t is the measure on R^n given by

6) $$p_t(A) = (2\pi t)^{-\frac{n}{2}} \int_A \exp[-\frac{|x|^2}{2t}] dx .$$

p_t is a probability measure. We shall show in the next few sections that the measures p_t can be given a simple and natural meaning when $n = \infty$. Defining F by 5) for $n = \infty$ it turns out that for suitable functions g the function u given by 3) does indeed satisfy 1). Further details will be found in section 4 of this paper.

There is no really good infinite dimensional analog of finite dimensional Lebesgue measure. Nevertheless several theorems of classical analysis on R^n in which Lebesgue measure plays a fundamental role have been successfully extended to the infinite dimensional case. In the infinite dimensional versions of these theorems it is the measures p_t which play a fundamental role. For $n = \infty$ the measure p_t is called Wiener measure with variance parameter t.

1. Cylinder set measures. Let V be a real vector space and V^* a vector space of linear functionals on V which separates points of V, i.e., for each vector x in V there is a vector y in V^* such that $\langle x,y\rangle \neq 0$. For example, we may take for V a real Banach space and for V^* the space of continuous linear functionals on V.

Definition 1. A cylinder set in V (also known as a tame set) is a set C of the form

$$C = \{x \in V:(\langle x,y_1\rangle, \ldots , \langle x,y_n\rangle) \in A\}$$

where A is a Borel set in R^n and y_j is in V^* for $j = 1,\ldots,n$. If K is a finite dimensional subspace of V^* containing $y_1,\ldots,y_n$ then C is said to be based on K.

Clearly C is also based on any other finite dimensional subspace of V^* containing K. If $z_1,\ldots,z_k$ is a basis for K and $y_j = \Sigma_{i=1}^{k} a_{ji} z_i$ $j = 1,\ldots,n$ let T be the transformation from R^k to R^n with matrix (a_{ji}). Then since the n tuple $(\langle x,y_1\rangle,\ldots,\langle x,y_n\rangle)$ is the transform by T of the k tuple $(\langle x,z_1\rangle,\ldots,\langle x,z_k\rangle)$ the cylinder set C may also be described as

$$C = \{x \in V:(\langle x,z_1\rangle,\ldots,\langle x,z_k\rangle) \in A_1\} \tag{7}$$

where $A_1 = T^{-1}A$. A_1 is, of course, a Borel set in R^k. Thus any cylinder set based on K can be described as in 7) with a fixed basis $z_1,\ldots,z_k$ of K. If $S:V \to R^k$ is the map

$Sx = (\langle x,z_1\rangle,\ldots,\langle x,z_k\rangle)$ then $C = S^{-1}(A_1)$ and it is clear that the collection $\mathcal{S}_K$ of cylinder sets based on K is a σ-ring. If K and K' are finite dimensional subspaces of V^* and $K \subset K'$ then $\mathcal{S}_K \subset \mathcal{S}_{K'}$. Denote by $\mathcal{R}$ the collection of all cylinder sets in V. Then $\mathcal{R} = \cup_K \mathcal{S}_K$ where K runs over all finite dimensional subspaces of V^*. Clearly $\mathcal{R}$ is a ring.

Definition. A tame function on V (also known as a cylinder function) is a function f which is measurable with respect to some $\mathcal{S}_K$. Such a function f is said to be based on K.

Definition. A non-negative set function μ defined on $\mathcal{R}$ is a cylinder set measure if

1) $\mu(V) = 1$

and 2) for each finite dimensional subspace $K \subset V^*$

μ is countably additive when restricted to the σ-ring $\mathcal{S}_K$.

Clearly a cylinder set measure is finitely additive on $\mathcal{R}$.

The cylinder set measure that we shall be most concerned with in this article is given in the following example.

Example. Let H be a real Hilbert space and H^* its topological dual space. A cylinder set in H can be desribed as

$$C = \{x \in H: ((x,y_1),\ldots,(x,y_n)) \in A\}$$

where $y_1,\ldots,y_n$ are orthonormal and A is a Borel set in R^n. If P is the orthogonal projection on H whose range F is the span of $y_1,\ldots,y_n$ then clearly

8) $C = \{x \in H : P x \in D\}$

where $D = C \cap F$

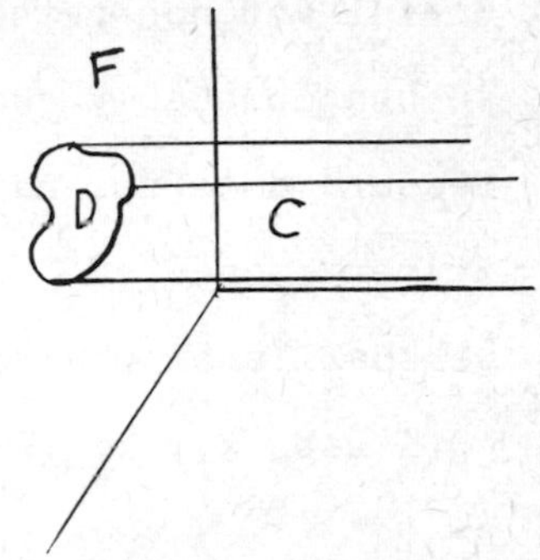

Define for each strictly positive number t

9) $\mu_t(C) = (2\pi t)^{-n} \int_D \exp[- |x|^2/2t]\, dx$

where n is the dimension of F and dx denotes Lebesgue measure on F. Then μ_t is well defined for identifying H with H^* for the moment, we observe that if C is based on the finite dimensional subspace K as well as F then it is also based on the span, L, of K and F. Moreover in L the set $C \cap L$ is a product, $C \cap L = D \times (L \ominus F)$ and since the measure p_t defined in the introduction is a product measure relative to any orthogonal decomposition and has total measure one equation 9) gives the same value to $\mu_t(C)$ whether C is considered to be based on F or L and hence on F or K.

We shall refer to μ_t as Gauss measure with variance parameter t. μ_t is a cylinder set measure for each strictly positive number t.

Remark 1. It is important to know whether a given cylinder set measure on a vector space V has a countably additive extension to the σ ring generated by the ring $\mathcal{R}$ of cylinder sets. Much of the literature on integration over function spaces is concerned directly or indirectly with this question. The absence of local compactness in infinite dimensional spaces permits the existence of useful and non-pathological cylinder set measures which do not have such a countably additive extension. We shall show first that Gauss measure does not have such a countably additive extension when the Hilbert space H is infinite dimensional. Then in the next section we shall show what can be done about it.

Let $x_1, x_2, \ldots$ be an orthonormal sequence in H. Let

$$A_n = \{x \in H : |(x, x_j)| \leq n,\ j = 1, \ldots, k_n\}.$$

No matter how the sequence k_n is chosen we have $\cup_{n=1}^{\infty} A_n = H$. But

$$\mu_t(A_n) = \left((2\pi t)^{-1/2} \int_{-n}^{n} \exp[-\,x^2/2t]dx\right)^{k_n}$$

so that for each n $\mu_t(A_n)$ can be made arbitrarily small by choosing k_n sufficiently large. Hence for a suitable choice of the sequence k_n we have $\Sigma_{n=1}^{\infty} \mu_t(A_n) < 1$ while on the other hand $\mu_t(H) = 1$. Thus μ_t is not countably additive on $\mathcal{R}$ and hence has no countably additive extension to the σ-ring generated by $\mathcal{R}$. In fact it is clear from the same argument that the outer μ_t measure of H is zero since $\Sigma_{n=1}^{\infty} \mu_t(A_n)$ can be made arbitrarily small by choosing the k_n sufficiently large.

This state of affairs is analogous to that which holds when one attempts to define Lebesgue measure on the rationals. Thus if one defines $m([a,b) \cap \text{rationals}) = b-a$ then m has no countably additive extension to a measure on sets of rational numbers. One may say that the reason for this is that the set of rationals is too small. In fact the outer m measure of the set of rationals is zero. Nevertheless the same formula defined for intervals of real numbers yields a countably additive extension - Lebesgue measure. We shall show in the next section that when H is completed in a suitable way the formula defining Gauss measure also yields a countably additive extension - Wiener measure.

2. Measurable norms and countable additivity.

In this section we shall define and prove the countable additivity of abstract Wiener measure. Gauss measure plays a fundamental role. Since all statements here are independent of the value of the variance parameter t we shall put $t = 1$ and write simply μ instead of μ_1 for Gauss measure with variance parameter one. This section is largely an adaptation of results of [4] and [6].

Definition. Let H be a real Hilbert space (norm $|\ |$.) A semi-norm $\|\cdot\|$ on H is called measurable if for every number $\epsilon > 0$ there is a finite dimensional projection P_0 on H such that

10) $$\mu(\{x \in H : \|Px\| > \epsilon\}) < \epsilon$$

whenever P is a finite dimensional projection orthogonal to P_0. A measurable norm is a measurable semi-norm which is a norm.

We note that $\{x \in H : \|Px\| > \epsilon\}$ is a cylinder set based on the range of P so that 10) makes sense.

Examples. 1) The Hilbert norm is not a measurable norm since μ is orthogonally invariant and consequently $\mu(\{x \in H: |Px| > \epsilon\})$ depends only on the rank of P.

2) Let A be a symmetric compact operator on a separable real Hilbert space H with square summable eigenvalues (i.e. a symmetric Hilbert-Schmidt operator.) Let $\|x\| = |Ax|$. Then $\|\cdot\|$ is a measurable semi-norm. For let $e_1, e_2, \ldots$ be an O.N. basis of H which diagonalizes A. Say $A e_j = \lambda_j e_j$ where

$\sum_{j=1}^{\infty} \lambda_j^2 < \infty$. Given $\epsilon > 0$ we choose P_0 to be the projection onto the span of $e_1, \ldots, e_n$ where n is chosen so that $\sum_{j>n} \lambda_j^2 < \epsilon^3$.

If P is a finite dimensional projection orthogonal to P_0 then since $\| Px \|^2$ is a cylinder function we may integrate it with respect to μ getting

$$\int_H \| Px \|^2 \, d\mu(x) = \int_H (PA^2Px, x) \, d\mu(x) .$$

The integral makes sense since $\| Px \|^2$ is a measurable function with respect to S_K $(K = PH)$ and μ is countably additive on S_K. (Here we have identified $H \equiv H^*$.) The integrand is a symmetric quadratic form of finite rank. Upon diagonalizing it with respect to an O.N. basis and using $(2\pi)^{-1/2} \int_{-\infty}^{\infty} s^2 \exp[-s^2/2] ds = 1$ we obtain for the value of the integral the sum of the eigenvalues of PA^2P.

But for any bounded operator T and any pair $\{e_j\}$, $\{f_k\}$ of O.N. bases of H there holds by Fubini's theorem

$$\text{11)} \qquad \Sigma_j |Te_j|^2 = \Sigma_j \Sigma_k |(f_k, Te_j)|^2$$

$$= \Sigma_k \Sigma_j |(T^* f_k, e_j)|^2$$

$$= \Sigma_k |T^* f_k|^2$$

whether these sums are finite or infinite. We recall that if the sum is finite for some O.N. basis $\{e_j\}$ then the bounded operator T is said to be of Hilbert-Schmidt type. Equation 11) shows that T^* is of Hilbert-Schmidt type when T is and a double application of 11) shows that the sum $\Sigma_j |T e_j|^2$ is independent of the choice of O.N. basis. The square root of this sum, called the Hilbert-Schmidt norm, is denoted by $\|T\|_2$. If B is bounded and T is of Hilbert-Schmidt type then clearly $\|BT\|_2 \leq \|B\| \, \|T\|_2$ and $\|TB\|_2 = \|B^* T^*\|_2 \leq \|B^*\| \, \|T^*\|_2$ $= \|B\| \, \|T\|_2$.

Now the sum of the eigenvalues of PA^2P may be written $\Sigma_j(PA^2Pe_j, e_j)$ if $\{e_j\}$ is an O.N. basis of H consisting of eigenvectors of PA^2P. But this sum is just $\Sigma_j |APe_j|^2$. Thus, since $(I - P_0)P = P$ we have

$$\begin{aligned} \int_H \|Px\|^2 d\mu(x) &= \|AP\|_2^2 \\ &= \|A(I - P_0)P\|_2^2 \\ &\leq \|A(I - P_0)\|_2^2 \\ &= \Sigma_{j>n} \lambda_j^2 \\ &< \epsilon^3 . \end{aligned}$$

Hence

$$\epsilon^2 \mu(\{x \in H : \|Px\| > \epsilon\}) \leq \int_H \|Px\|^2 d\mu(x) < \epsilon^3 .$$

This establishes that $\|\cdot\|$ is a measurable semi-norm.

If in addition A is one to one then $|Ax|$ is a measurable norm.

In order to establish that a given semi-norm is measurable it is convenient to have the following theorem.

Theorem 1. Let $\|x\|_n$ be an increasing sequence of tame semi-norms on H. Suppose that for each strictly positive real number ϵ

$$\lim_{n\to\infty} \mu(\{x \in H : \|x\|_n \leq \epsilon\}) > 0$$

Then $\lim_{n\to\infty} \|x\|_n$ exists for each x in H and the limit is a measurable semi-norm.

Note: The sequence $\mu(\{x \in H : \|x\|_n \leq \epsilon\})$ is clearly decreasing so its limit exists.

Lemma 1.1 Let S be a compact convex set in E_n. Let p_1, p_2, p_3 be three parallel hyperplanes in E_n such that p_2 lies between p_1, and p_3 (i.e. p_2 is in the convex closure of p_1 and p_3). Let $S_i = S \cap p_i$, $i = 1,2,3$ and let m denote $n-1$ dimensional Lebesgue measure. Then $m(S_2) \geq \min\{m(S_1), m(S_3)\}$.

Proof. This is a simple consequence of the Brunn-Minkowski theorem. (See [1, § 41].)

Lemma 1.2 Let F be a subspace of a finite dimensional real Hilbert space K. Denote by μ and μ' Gauss measure in K and F respectively. Let B be a convex centrally symmetric set in K and let C be a convex cylinder in K of the form $C = D \times F$ where D is a convex set in $F^{\perp}$. If B is contained in C then $\mu(B) \leq \mu(C)\mu'(F \cap B)$. In particular if $C = K$ then

$\mu(B) \leq \mu'(F \cap B)$.

Proof. Let $x \neq 0$ be in $F^{\perp}$ and denote by P the orthogonal projection on K with range F. Let $r > 0$ and let C_r denote the circular cylinder $\{x : \|Px\| \leq r\}$. If k is the dimension of F then we denote by m, k-dimensional Lebesgue measure. In the $k+1$ dimensional subspace G spanned by x and F the previous lemma may be applied to the three hyperplanes $-x+F$, F and $x+F$ and to the convex set $S_r = G \cap B \cap C_r$ to obtain

$$m(F \cap S_r) \geq \min \{m((-x+F) \cap S_r),\ m((x+F) \cap S_r)\}.$$

(The possible lack of compactness of S_r clearly does not affect the application of Lemma 1.1). Since S_r is centrally symmetric we have $m(F \cap S_r) \geq m((x+F) \cap S_r)$. Hence

$$\begin{aligned}
\mu'((x+F) \cap B) &= \mu'((x+F) \cap (G \cap B)) \\
&= (2\pi)^{-k/2} \int_0^{\infty} e^{-r^2/2}\, d_r m((x+F) \cap S_r) \\
&= (2\pi)^{-k/2} \int_0^{\infty} m((x+F) \cap S_r) e^{-r^2/2}\, r\, dr \\
&\leq (2\pi)^{-k/2} \int_0^{\infty} m(F \cap S_r) e^{-r^2/2}\, r\, dr \\
&\leq \mu'(F \cap B).
\end{aligned}$$

Now let ν be Gauss measure in $F^{\perp}$. Then μ is the product of μ' and ν. Now the projection of B on $F^{\perp}$ is contained in the projection of C on $F^{\perp}$ which is exactly $C \cap F^{\perp} = D$. Hence

$$\mu(B) = \int_{F^\perp} \mu'((x+F)\cap B)\,d\nu(x)$$
$$= \int_D \mu'((x+F)\cap B)\,d\nu(x)$$
$$\leq \int_D \mu'(F\cap B)\,d\nu(x)$$
$$\leq \mu'(F\cap B)\nu(D) = \mu'(F\cap B)\mu(C).$$

Corollary 1.3 If $\|\cdot\|$ is a semi-norm on H and P and Q are finite dimensional projections with $P \leq Q$ then for all numbers $a > 0$

$$\mu(\{x\in H : \|Qx\| \leq a\}) \leq \mu(\{x\in H : \|Px\| \leq a\}).$$

Proof. Take $K = QH$, $F = PH$, $B = \{x \in QH : \|Qx\| \leq a\}$. Then the preceding lemma yields

$$\mu(\{x\in H : \|Qx\| \leq a\}) = \mu_K(\{x\in K : \|Qx\| \leq a\})$$
$$= \mu_K(B)$$
$$\leq \mu'(F\cap B)$$
$$= \mu(\{x\in H : \|Px\| \leq a\})$$

where norm μ_K denotes Gauss measure in K.

Proof of Theorem 1. We shall write $\mu(f(x) > a)$ instead of $\mu(\{x\in H : f(x) > a\})$ to shorten the notation.

Let y be a unit vector in H and let Q be any finite dimensional projection containing y in its range. If P is the projection given by $Px = (x,y)y$ then $P \leq Q$. For any semi-norm we have by

Corollary 1.3

12) $$\mu(\|Qx\| \leq 1) \leq \mu(|(x,y)|\ \|y\| \leq 1)$$

since $\|Px\| = |(x,y)|\ \|y\|$.

Apply 12) to the tame semi-norm $\|x\|_n$ choosing Q to be a finite dimensional projection whose range contains both y and the subspace on which $\|\cdot\|_n$ is based. Then $\|Qx\|_n = \|x\|_n$ and we obtain

13) $$0 < c \leq \mu(\|x\|_n \leq 1) \leq \mu(|(x,y)|\ \|y\|_n \leq 1)$$

where the choice $c > 0$ may be made independently of n by the hypothesis of the theorem. Now the set $\{x \in H: |(x,y)|\ \|y\|_n \leq 1\}$ is a cylinder set based on the one dimensional subspace spanned by y. Choose b such that

$$(2\pi)^{-1/2} \int_{-b}^{b} \exp\,[-s^2/2]\, ds = c .$$

It follows from 13) that, assuming $\|y\|_n \neq 0$, $(\|y\|_n)^{-1} \geq b$. Or in other words that $\|y\|_n \leq b^{-1}$ for all unit vectors y and all n. Thus the semi-norms $\|\cdot\|_n$ are uniformly bounded on the unit sphere of H and since they form an increasing sequence they converge on all of H. Denote the limit by $\|x\|_0$. It is clearly a semi-norm.

Now we shall show that $\|x\|_0$ is measurable. Let $\epsilon > 0$ and put $a = \lim_{n\to\infty} \mu(\|x\|_n \leq \epsilon)$. Then $a > 0$. We may assume $0 < \epsilon < 1$. Put $\eta = \epsilon/(2-\epsilon)$ and choose N such that

$$|\mu(\|x\|_N \leq \epsilon) - a| \leq \eta a .$$

Then since the $\|x\|_n$ form an increasing sequence we have

$$|\mu(\|x\|_n \leq \epsilon) - a| \leq \eta a$$

for all $n \geq N$. Now $\|\cdot\|_N$ is a tame semi-norm based, say, on $P_0 H$ where P_0 is a finite dimensional projection. Let P be a finite dimensional projection orthogonal to P_0. Put $Q = P + P_0$. Let $m \geq N$ and in the subspace $K = QH$ consider the following convex centrally symmetric sets:

$$B_1 = \{x \in K : \|x\|_N \leq \epsilon\}$$

$$B_2 = \{x \in K : \|x\|_m \leq \epsilon\}.$$

Since $\|x\|_N \leq \|x\|_m$ we have $B_2 \subset B_1$. Let $F = PH$. Since $\|x\|_N = \|P_0 x\|_N$ B_1 is a convex cylinder with generators parallel to F. By Lemma 1.2

$$\mu_K(B_2) \leq \mu_K(B_1)\, \mu'(B_2 \cap F)$$

where μ_K is Gauss measure in K and μ' is Gauss measure in F. In terms of Gauss measure on H this reads

$$\mu(\|Qx\|_m \leq \epsilon) \leq \mu(\|x\|_N \leq \epsilon)\, \mu(\|Px\|_m \leq \epsilon).$$

If R is a finite dimensional projection with $R \geq Q$ such that $\|\cdot\|_m$ is based on the range of R then $\|Rx\|_m = \|x\|_m$ for all x in H and by Corollary 1.3 there holds

$\mu(\|x\|_m \leq \epsilon) \leq \mu(\|Qx\|_m \leq \epsilon)$. Hence

$$\mu(\|x\|_m \leq \epsilon) \leq \mu(\|x\|_N \leq \epsilon)\, \mu(\|Px\|_m \leq \epsilon)$$

for all $m \geq N$. Thus

$$(1-\eta)a \leq \mu(\|x\|_m \leq \epsilon) \leq (1+\eta)a\,\mu(\|Px\|_m \leq \epsilon).$$

Hence

$$\mu(\|Px\|_m \leq \epsilon) \geq \frac{1-\eta}{1+\eta} = 1-\epsilon$$

for all $m \geq N$. Now in the subspace PH the set $\{x \in PH : \|Px\|_0 = \epsilon\}$ is a set of (Lebesgue and Gauss) measure zero. Hence we may pass to the limit in the last inequality letting $m \to \infty$ (it clearly suffices to use standard measure theory arguments in the subspace PH only) to obtain $\mu(\|Px\|_0 \leq \epsilon) \geq 1-\epsilon$ or equivalently $\mu(\|Px\|_0 > \epsilon) < \epsilon$. This establishes the measurability of $\|\cdot\|_0$.

Remark 2. Any measurable norm $\|\cdot\|$ on H is continuous with respect to the H norm $|\ |$. For let P_0 be a finite dimensional projection on H such that

$$\mu(\{x \in H : \|Px\| > 1/2\}) < 1/2$$

whenever P is a finite dimensional projection orthogonal to P_0. Let b be the positive number satisfying $(2\pi)^{-1/2} \int_{|s|>b} \exp(-s^2/2)ds = 1/2$. Let y be a unit vector orthogonal to P_0 and put $Px = (x,y)y$. Then $\|Px\| = |(x,y)|\ \|y\|$ and we have

$$\mu(\{x \in H : |(x,y)|\ \|y\| > 1/2\}) < 1/2.$$

The set in the last line is based on a one dimensional subspace and from the definition of μ the last line may be written, assuming $\|y\| \neq 0$,

$$(2\pi)^{-1/2} \int_{|s|>(2\|y\|)^{-1}} \exp[-s^2/2]ds < 1/2 .$$

Hence $(2\|y\|)^{-1} > b$. Thus $\|y\| < b/2$. Hence for any vector x in $(I - P_0)H$ we have $\|x\| \leq (b/2)\,|x|$. But the restriction of $\|\cdot\|$ to the finite dimensional subspace P_0H is automatically continuous with respect to $|\cdot|$. Hence for some constant $a \geq b/2$ we have $\|x\| \leq a\,|x|$ for x in either P_0H or $(I - P_0)H$. It follows that for x in P_0H and z in $(I - P_0)H$ $\|x+z\| \leq \|x\| + \|z\| \leq a\,(|x| + |z|) \leq a\sqrt{2}\,|x+z|$ which establishes the assertion of this remark.

Remark 3. Let $\|\cdot\|$ be a measurable norm on H and denote by B the completion of H with respect to $\|\cdot\|$. The injection map $i: H \rightarrow B$ is continuous by virtue of the preceding remark and of course has dense range. Its adjoint $i^*: B^* \rightarrow H^*$ is consequently one to one. We shall identify B^* with a subset of H^* henceforth, with the aid of the map i^*. Gauss measure μ on H induces a cylinder set measure m on B simply by the prescription that for any integer n and for $y_1, \ldots, y_n \in B^*$ and any Borel set A in R^n

13) $$m(\{x \in B : (\langle x,y_1\rangle, \ldots, \langle x,y_n\rangle) \in A\})$$
$$= \mu(\{x \in H : (\langle x,y_1\rangle, \ldots, \langle x,y_n\rangle) \in A).$$

Thus m and μ are given by the same "formula" but on different sets.

Theorem 2. Let $\|\cdot\|$ be a measurable norm on a real separable Hilbert space H. Denote by B the completion of H with respect to $\|\cdot\|$ and by m the cylinder set measure on the ring $\mathcal{R}$ of cylinder sets of B induced by Gauss measure on H. Then m is countably additive on $\mathcal{R}$.

Lemma 2.1. Let $\|\cdot\|$ be a measurable norm on a real separable Hilbert space H. Let $\{a_j\}_{j=0,1,\ldots}$ be an arbitrary sequence of strictly positive real numbers. Then there exists a sequence $\{Q_j\}_{j=0,1,\ldots}$ of mutually orthogonal finite dimensional projections on H with sum equal to the identity operator such that the sum $\Sigma_{j=0}^{\infty} a_j \|Q_j x\|$ converges pointwise on H to a measurable norm $\|\cdot\|_1$.

Proof. We remark that the interest in this lemma lies in the case where the a_j approach $+\infty$. For the sake of a minor simplification we assume, without loss of generality, that $a_j \geq 1$ for all j.

From the definition of measurable norm there exists a finite dimensional projection P_n for each $n \geq 1$ such that

$$\mu(\|Px\| > 1/(a_n 2^n)) < 1/(a_n 2^n) \leq 2^{-n}$$

whenever P is a finite dimensional projection orthogonal to P_n. By enlarging the range of P_n if necessary we may assume that the P_n form an increasing sequence and converge strongly to the identity operator.

Let $Q_0 = P_1$ and $Q_n = P_{n+1} - P_n$ for $n = 1,2, \ldots$. Then the projections Q_n are mutually orthogonal finite dimensional projections and $\Sigma_{j=0}^{\infty} Q_j = I$. Moreover for $n \geq 1$ Q_n is orthogonal to P_n; so

$$\mu(a_n \|Q_n x\| > 2^{-n}) < 2^{-n} \qquad n = 1,2, \ldots .$$

Let $\|x\|_n = \Sigma_{j=0}^{n} a_j \|Q_j x\| \qquad n = 1,2, \ldots .$

Then $\|\cdot\|_n$ is a tame semi-norm. We shall show that the hypothesis of Theorem 1 applies to this increasing sequence. Let ϵ be a strictly positive real number less than one. Choose an integer $k \geq 1$ such that $2^{-k} \leq \epsilon/2$. Let $n > k$. Then

$$\{x \in H: \|x\|_n \leq \epsilon\} \supset \{x \in H: \|x\|_k \leq \epsilon/2\} \cap \{x \in H: \Sigma_{j=k+1}^{n} a_j \|Q_j x\| \leq \epsilon/2\}.$$

Moreover, all three sets are cylinder sets and the two sets on the right are based on mutually orthogonal subspaces, namely on $P_{k+1}H$ and $(P_{n+1} - P_{k+1})H$ respectively. Hence the Gauss measure of the indicated intersection is the product of the Gauss measures. Thus

$$\mu(\|x\|_n \leq \epsilon) \geq \mu(\|x\|_k \leq \epsilon/2)\ \mu(\Sigma_{j=k+1}^{n} a_j \|Q_j x\| \leq \epsilon/2).$$

Now

$$\{x \in H : \Sigma_{j=k+1}^{n} a_j \|Q_j x\| > \epsilon/2\} \subset \cup_{j=k+1}^{n} \{x \in H : a_j \|Q_j x\| > 2^{-j}\}$$

and all these sets are cylinder sets contained in a fixed σ-ring $S_{P_{n+1}H}$ on which μ is additive (in fact countably additive). Hence

$$\begin{aligned} \mu(\Sigma_{j=k+1}^{n} a_j \|Q_j x\| > \epsilon/2) &\leq \Sigma_{j=k+1}^{n} \mu(a_j \|Q_j x\| > 2^{-j}) \\ &\leq \Sigma_{j=k+1}^{n} 2^{-j} \\ &\leq 2^{-k} \\ &\leq \epsilon/2 \leq 1/2 . \end{aligned}$$

Thus $\mu(\Sigma_{j=k+1}^{n} a_j \|Q_j x\| \leq \epsilon/2) \geq 1/2$. Hence

$$\mu(\|x\|_n \leq \epsilon) \geq (1/2)\ \mu(\|x\|_k \leq \epsilon/2) \qquad n > k .$$

In the subspace $P_{k+1}H$ the set $\{x \in P_{k+1}H : \|x\|_k \leq \epsilon/2\}$ is clearly a convex set with a non-empty interior. Hence $\mu(\|x\|_k < \epsilon/2) > 0$. Consequently

$\lim_{n\to\infty} \mu(\|x\|_n \leq \epsilon) \geq (1/2)\, \mu(\|x\|_k \leq \epsilon/2) > 0$. By Theorem 1 $\lim_{n\to\infty} \|x\|_n$ exists for each x in H and is a measurable semi-norm. For any x in H $Q_j x \neq 0$ for some j so that the limit is a measurable norm.

Lemma 2.2 *Let $\|x\|$ be a measurable norm on H and let B be the completion of H in this norm. There exists a measurable norm $\|x\|_0$ on H such that for each real number $r > 0$, the closure in B of the set $S_r = \{x \in H : \|x\|_0 \leq r\}$ is compact in B.*

Proof. Let $\{a_j\}_{j=0,1,\ldots}$ be a sequence of strictly positive real numbers such that $\Sigma_{j=0}^{\infty} a_j^{-1}$ is finite. Let $\|x\|_0 = \Sigma_{j=0}^{\infty} a_j \|Q_j x\|$ where the Q_j are those projections given in Lemma 2.1.

It suffices to show that if x_n is a sequence in H with $\|x_n\|_0 \leq r$ for $n = 1, 2, \ldots,$ then some subsequence is Cauchy with respect to $\|\cdot\|$. Now the restriction of $\|Q_j x\|$ to the range K_j of the finite dimensional projection Q_j is a norm on K_j equivalent to the Euclidean norm, and since $\|Q_j x_n\| \leq r a_j^{-1}$ for all n, there is a subsequence of the sequence x_n such that $Q_j x_n$ is Cauchy with respect to $\|\cdot\|$. By diagonalization and dropping to a subsequence, we may assume that $Q_j x_n$ is Cauchy for all j.

A measurable norm is strongly continuous by corollary 1.3. Consequently, $\| x_n - x_m \| \leq \Sigma_{j=0}^{\infty} \| Q_j(x_n - x_m) \|$. Each term of the sum goes to zero as n and m go to infinity and is dominated by $2ra_j^{-1}$. Hence, $\| x_n - x_m \| \to 0$.

Proof of Theorem 2. Since $m(B)$ is finite it suffices, as is well known, to prove that m is continuous from below at B. Since Gauss measure on a finite dimensional Euclidean space is regular the measure of a cylinder set in B can be approximated from above by open cylinder sets. (Weakly open and strongly open are the same for cylinder sets.) Consequently, m is countably additive on R if for every covering of B by a sequence of open cylinder sets T_n there holds $\Sigma_{n=1}^{\infty} m(T_n) \geq 1$. In order for this condition to hold, it is sufficient that for every real number $\epsilon > 0$ there exists a weakly compact set C_ϵ in B such that $m(T) < \epsilon$ for any tame set T disjoint from C_ϵ. Indeed, if T_n is a covering of B by a sequence of open tame sets, then since the T_n are also weakly open, a finite number, say $T_1, \ldots, T_N$, cover C_ϵ, and consequently,

$$\begin{aligned}\sum_{n=1}^{\infty} m(T_n) &\geq \sum_{n=1}^{\infty} m(T_n) \\ &\geq m\left(\bigcup_{n=1}^{N} T_n\right) \\ &= 1 - m\left(B - \bigcup_{n=1}^{N} T_n\right) \\ &\geq 1 - \epsilon ,\end{aligned}$$

which in view of the arbitrariness of ϵ, implies that $\Sigma_{n=1}^{\infty} m(T_n) \geq 1$.

Before proceeding further, we remark that the preceding argument is the basic one used in much of the literature to prove countable additivity of cylinder set measures. When the underlying space B is itself a dual space of a Banach space or nuclear space, the sets C_ϵ are taken as closed balls in B. However, in the present case, B is not necessarily a dual space. Our proof from here parallels Wiener's proof [13] of the countable additivity of Wiener measure. The sets C_ϵ will be strongly compact.

Let $\|\cdot\|_0$ be the measurable norm on H whose existence is asserted in Lemma 2.2. Let ϵ be a strictly positive real number less than one. From the definition of measurable norm it follows that there exists a finite dimensional projection P_0 on H such that for any finite dimensional projection P orthogonal to P_0 there holds $\mu(\|Px\|_0 > 1) < \epsilon/2$. Since μ is countably additive on S_{P_0H} it follows that for some sufficiently large number r we have $\mu(\|P_0x\|_0 > r - 1) < \epsilon/2$. If Q is a finite dimensional projection satisfying $Q \geq P_0$ put $P = Q - P_0$ and observe that the inequality $\|Qx\|_0 \leq \|P_0x\|_0 + \|Px\|_0$ implies that

$$14) \quad \mu(\|Qx\|_0 > r) \leq \mu(\|P_0x\|_0 > r-1) + \mu(\|Px\|_0 > 1) < \epsilon .$$

Moreover, if P_1 is any finite dimensional projection we may choose a finite dimensional projection Q satisfying both $Q \geq P_1$ and $Q \geq P_0$ and obtain, using 14) and Corollary 1.3

$$\mu(\|P_1 x\|_0 > r) < \epsilon$$

Now let C_ϵ be the closure in B of $\{x \in H: \|x\|_0 \leq r\}$. By lemma 2.2 C_ϵ is (strongly) compact in B. Let T be a cylinder set of B disjoint from C_ϵ and suppose that T is based on the finite dimensional subspace K of B^*. Suppose, moreover, that T is given as in the left side of the equation 13) where $y_1,\ldots,y_n$ are O.N. in H^* and form a basis of K. Under the usual isomorphism of H^* with H (we do not identify them now) the O.N. vectors $\{y_j\}$ go over into O.N. vectors $\{x_j\}$ respectively. Let L be the span of $x_1,\ldots,x_n$. Thus $K \subset B^* \subset H^*$ and $L \subset H \subset B$. Let P_1 be the projection of H onto L. Thus $P_1 x = \Sigma_{j=1}^{n} \langle x, y_j \rangle x_j$ for x in H. The set $\{x \in H : \|P_1 x\|_0 \leq r\} = \{x \in H: \|\Sigma_{j=1}^{n} \langle x, y_j\rangle x_j\|_0 \leq r\}$ is a cylinder set in H based on K as is also $T \cap H$. Thus the generators of these two cylinder sets are both perpendicular to L. Moreover, their intersections with L are $L \cap C_\epsilon$ and $L \cap T$ respectively and are thus disjoint. Hence $\{x \in H: \|P_1 x\|_0 \leq r\}$ is disjoint from $T \cap H$. Thus $T \cap H \subset \{x \in H : \|P_1 x\|_0 > r\}$ and $m(T) = \mu(T \cap H) \leq \mu(\|P_1 x\|_0 > r) < \epsilon$. This concludes the proof of Theorem 2.

Remark 4. By virtue of Theorem 2 the cylinder set measure m on $\mathcal{R}$ can be extended to a countably additive measure p on the σ-ring $\mathcal{S}$ generated by $\mathcal{R}$. It is not difficult to see that $\mathcal{S}$ contains all closed balls, hence all open balls, hence all open sets since B is separable. Hence $\mathcal{S}$ is the Borel field of B (i.e. the σ-ring generated by the open sets of B.) We mention without proof that there exists no measurable norm on an inseparable Hilbert space so our restriction to separable Hilbert spaces is essential. We also mention that the measure p assigns positive measure to all non empty open sets of B so it is reasonably related to the topology of B. See [6].

A triple (i, H, B) where $i : H \to B$ is a continuous injection of the real Hilbert space H into the real Banach space B with dense range is called an <u>abstract Wiener space</u> if the B norm pulled back to H is a measurable norm. The probability measure p on the Borel field of B whose existence is assured by Theorem 2 is called Wiener measure (or abstract Wiener measure to distinguish it from classical Wiener measure) and reduces to classical Wiener measure when (i, H, B) is chosen as follows. Let $\mathcal{C}$ denote the space of real valued continuous functions on [0,1] which vanish at zero. Denote by $\mathcal{C}'$ the set of those x in $\mathcal{C}$ which are absolutely continuous and for which $|x|^2 = \int_0^1 (\frac{dx}{dt})^2 dt$ is finite. Then $\mathcal{C}'$ is a Hilbert space. The norm on $\mathcal{C}'$ given by $\|x\| = \sup_{0 \leq t \leq 1} |x(t)|$ is a measurable norm (see [4]) and the completion of $\mathcal{C}'$ in this norm is clearly identifiable with $\mathcal{C}$. Taking $H = \mathcal{C}'$ and $B = \mathcal{C}$ the abstract Wiener measure p on $\mathcal{C}$ turns out to be exactly the classical Wiener measure.

We remark finally that any separable Banach space can arise as the third element of some abstract Wiener space (see [6].)

3. Potential theory. In this section we shall survey some results on infinite dimensional potential theory. For surveys of other topics in classical analysis over infinite dimensional spaces and for some very recent developments see [1,2,3,5,8,9,10]. Proofs of the statements in this section may be found in [7].

Let (i,H,B) be an abstract Wiener space. Theorem 2 of the preceding section is applicable with no essential change if one starts with Gauss measure μ_t on H with variance parameter $t > 0$ instead of variance parameter one. One thereby obtains for each $t > 0$ a probability measure p_t on the Borel field of B. Defining p_0 to be the probability measure on B concentrated at the origin one may verify the semi-group property: $p_t * p_s = p_{t+s}$ for $t, s \geq 0$ where $*$ denotes convolution. Associated with this semi-group of probability measures in a well known way is a Markov process with state space B which may be called an infinite dimensional Brownian motion. In terms of this process much of potential theory on B can be developed, including for example the Dirichlet problem for reasonable open subsets of B, where the notion of harmonic function can be defined in a generalized sense with the aid of the Markov process. We shall not discuss these probabilistic matters here (see [7]) but rather we shall discuss some more analytic questions.

When H is finite dimensional the H norm is clearly measurable (and all norms are equivalent) and clearly B = H. In this case the measures p_t are exactly those given in the introduction in equation 6) and it is well known that the measures p_t, acting via convolution on some suitable space of functions on H, e.g. the space $\mathcal{a}$ of bounded uniformly continuous functions on H, form a strongly continuous semi-group of contraction operators. Its infinitesimal generator is some extension of the Laplacian. More precisely, if f and its second derivatives are in $\mathcal{a}$ then

14) $$\text{strong} \lim_{t\downarrow o} \frac{p_t * f - f}{t} = \frac{1}{2} \Delta f$$

Thus one may write $p_t* = \exp[t\Delta/2]$. This is of course what is behind equations 1), 3), 5) of the introduction, since, informally, $\int_o^\infty \exp[t\Delta/2]\, dt = (\Delta/2)^{-1}$.

When H is infinite dimensional we may ask to what extent the above discussion goes through. In particular is the semi-group p_t, regarded as acting by convolution in some function space on B, strongly continuous and is its infinitesimal generator reasonably related to the Laplacian?

We recall that a trace class operator T on a Hilbert space H may be defined as a product, T = AB, of two Hilbert-Schmidt operators A and B. (See Example 2 in section 2 for the definition of Hilbert-Schmidt operator). For a trace class operator T the trace of T, $\sum_{j=1}^{\infty} (T e_j, e_j)$, is well defined for any O.N. basis $\{e_j\}$ since $\sum_{j=1}^{\infty} |(Te_j, e_j)| \leq \Sigma_{j=1}^{\infty} |Be_j|\,|A^*e_j| \leq ||B||_2 ||A^*||_2 < \infty$ and it is not hard to verify that the value of the sum is independent of the choice of O.N. basis. Now if u is a real valued function defined on an open set V in H then we say that u is twice Frechet differentiable at a point x_o in V with Frechet derivative T at x_o if T is a bounded operator on H such that

$$(Th,k) = \frac{d}{ds}\frac{d}{dt} \quad u(x_o + sh + tk)\Big|_{s=t=o} \qquad h, k \in H$$

and if these derivatives exist uniformly for $|h| \leq 1$, $|k| \leq 1$. As we know, when H is finite dimensional the operator T corresponds to the matrix $T_{ij} = \partial^2 u/\partial x_i \, \partial x_j$ and $\Delta u(x_o) = \text{trace } T$. Denoting T by $D^2u(x_o)$ we may now give a reasonable definition of the Laplacian of u when u is a real valued function defined on an open subset V of an infinite dimensional Hilbert space H and $D^2u(x)$ is a trace class operator on H for each x-. namely

$$\Delta\, u\, (x) = \text{trace } D^2u(x)$$

Actually we are concerned with functions on B rather than H. But for such a function v, defined in a B neighborhood of a point x_o of B the function $u(h) = v(x_o+h)$, $h \in H$ is defined in an H neighborhood of zero and the second Frechet derivative of v <u>in H directions</u> at x_o may be defined simply as $D^2v(x_o) = D^2u(o)$. Thus $D^2v(x_o)$ is an operator on H and if it should be trace class then we may form the Laplacian of v : $\Delta v(x_o) = \text{trace } D^2v(x_o)$.

<u>Theorem 3</u> <u>Let</u> (i, H, B) <u>be an abstract Wiener space and let</u> $\mathfrak{a}$ <u>be the Banach space of bounded uniformly continuous real valued functions on</u> B. <u>For</u> f <u>in</u> A <u>define</u> $P_t f = p_t * f$. P_t <u>is</u>

a strongly continuous contraction semi-group on A. Let S be its infinitesimal generator. The functions v in the domain of S satisfying the following conditions are dense in the domain of S in the graph norm.

i. $D^2v(x)$ is trace class on H for each x in B.

ii. $Sv = \frac{1}{2} \Delta v$

Remark 5 Theorem 3 shows that in the strongest reasonable sense the operators P_t deserve to be denoted exp $[t \Delta/2]$. One should expect then that the measure F on B defined by $F(A) = \int_0^\infty p_t(A)dt$ represents the fundamental solution to Poisson's equation 1). That this is actually the case follows from the next theorem.

Theorem 4. Let g be a bounded real valued function on B with bounded support such that for some $\alpha > 0$ g is in Lip_α, i.e.,

$$|g(x) - g(y)| \leq \text{const } ||x-y||^\alpha \text{ for all } x, y \text{ in } B.$$

Let u be the potential of g i.e. $u = F*g$. Then $D^2u(x)$ exists and is of Hilbert-Schmidt type for all x in D.

If $\alpha = 1$ then $D^2u(x)$ is trace class for all x in B and

$$\frac{1}{2} \Delta u(x) = - g(x) \qquad x \in B.$$

<u>Remark 6</u> The preceding two theorems are regularity theorems which show a resemblance to known regularity theorems in finite dimensional potential theory. But these theorems address themselves to a new type of regularity question which is not relevant in finite dimensions. Namely, even if $D^2u(x)$ exists as a bounded operator (where $u = F*g$ say) it is pertinent to ask, when H is infinite dimensional, whether $D^2u(x)$ is trace class. Or if not, is it of Hilbert-Schmidt type or compact, etc? Such a question has no interesting content when H is finite dimensional since the answer is automatically yes. Moreover there is a further interesting deviation from finite dimensional regularity properties which are connected with this type of question. In finite dimensional potential theory the smoothness of u at x_o depends only on the smoothness of g in an arbitrarily small neighborhood of x_o. But for any infinite dimensional abstract Wiener space (i,H,B) there exists a bounded continuous function g on B with support in the annulus $1 \leq ||x|| \leq 2$ such that, although its potential u(x) is analytic in a neighborhood of the origin, nevertheless $D^2u(o)$ is not trace class. Thus in view of Theorem 4 the behavior of $D^2u(x)$ with respect to the property of being trace class is not determined by the local behavior of g near x. Thus the principle of localizability is violated.

At the time of the present writing pointwise regularity properties similar to those above are under investigation for solutions to the Dirichlet problem in infinite dimensions. To someone familiar with the history of potential theory it will be apparent that the present state of infinite dimensional potential theory is about the same as that in which finite dimensional potential theory found itself at the beginning of this century.

1. Ju. L. Daleckii, Infinite-dimensional elliptic operators and the corresponding parabolic equations, Russian Math. Surveys v. 22 no. 4, 1-53 (1967).

2. Michael J. Fisher, Singular integral operators over a Hilbert space, Trans. Am. Math. Soc. v. 131 pp. 437-465 (1968)

3. I. M. Gelfand and N. Ya. Vilenkin, Some applications of harmonic analysis - augmented Hilbert spaces, Generalized Functions, vol. 4, New York, Academic Press, 1964.

4. L. Gross, Measurable functions on Hilbert space, Trans. Am. Math. Soc. v. 105 pp. 372-390 (1962)

5. ————, Classical analysis on a Hilbert space, in Analysis in Function Space, Chapter 4 pp. 51-68, M.I.T. Press 1964.

6. ————, Abstract Wiener spaces, in Proceedings of the Fifth Berkeley Symposium on Mathematical Statistics and Probability, 1965 Vol. 2 Part I, pp 31-42.

7. ————, Potential theory on Hilbert space, Jour. of Functional Anal. v. 1 pp. 123-181 (1967).

8. K. R. Parthasarathy, Probability in metric spaces, Academic Press, New York (1967)

9. M. A. Piech, A fundamental solution of the parabolic equation on Hilbert space, Jour. of Functional Analysis v.3 pp. 85-114 (1969)

10. Yu. V. Prohorov, The method of characteristic functionals, Proceedings of the Fourth Berkeley Symposium on Mathematical Statistics and Probability (1961) Vol. 2, pp. 403-419.

CONTENTS

Lectures in Modern Analysis and Applications I

MODERN METHODS AND NEW RESULTS IN COMPLEX ANALYSIS

A discussion of the compactification of the unit disc which is induced by the algebra of bounded analytic functions, especially Carleson's work on the corona theorem and the speaker's work on analytic subsets of the compactification.

Some of the most exciting work in several complex variables done in the past ten years centers around the solution of Levi's problem: to show that a pseudoconvex domain is holomorphically convex. Pseudoconvexity is a differential condition on the nature of the boundary; the latter implies the existence of many holomorphic functions. The key to the solution is the theorem of finite dimensionality of the cohomology groups of a coherent sheaf, proven by Grauert, Kohn, Hörmander. From this one can fully describe the analytic structure of a strongly pseudoconvex domain, and this gives rise to a method for studying isolated singularities of analytic spaces.

BANACH ALGEBRAS AND APPLICATIONS

Problems and methods in uniform approximation by holomorphic functions on compact sets in spaces of one or more complex variables.

3

Professor CHARLES E. RICKART, Yale University

A function algebra, which does not contain all continuous functions, may exhibit certain properties reminiscent of analycity. An example is the local maximum modulus principle proved by Hugo Rossi. This, along with various results, suggests the beginnings of an abstract analytic function theory. At this stage, the program is to obtain analogues of certain results from several complex variables.

TOPOLOGICAL LINEAR SPACES AND APPLICATIONS

Professor LARS HÖRMANDER, Institute for Advanced Study

For the Cauchy problem with data on a hyperplane there exists a unique solution for arbitrary data if and only if the equation is hyperbolic in the sense of Garding. When the hyperplane is characteristic there is no longer uniqueness, but we characterize the equations having a solution for arbitrary Cauchy data. This class contains all parabolic equations.

Professor F. TREVES, Purdue University

Local Cauchy problems for systems of linear PDEs with analytic coefficients, with data on noncharacteristic hypersurfaces, have always unique solutions. But these in general need not be distributions, they are ultradistributions. A simple proof of this fact is possible, based on general results about abstract differential equations (also valid for nonlinear ones), suitably adapted blowing up of small domains and ladders of functional (Banach) spaces. This allows a detailed description of the situation, including of the symbols of "fundamental solutions", and reveals the links with the problem of solvability in more classical sense.

GEOMETRIC AND QUALITATIVE ASPECTS OF ANALYSIS

* This lecture was presented by Professor James Eells.

Offsetdruck: Julius Beltz, Weinheim/Bergstr.

Bitte wenden / Continued

Vol. 72: The Syntax and Semantics of Infinitary Languages. Edited by J. Barwise. IV, 268 pages. 1968. DM 18,– / $ 5.00

Vol. 73: P. E. Conner, Lectures on the Action of a Finite Group. IV, 123 pages. 1968. DM 10,– / $ 2.80

Vol. 74: A. Fröhlich, Formal Groups. IV, 140 pages. 1968. DM 12,– / $ 3.30

Vol. 75: G. Lumer, Algèbres de fonctions et espaces de Hardy. VI, 80 pages. 1968. DM 8,– / $ 2.20

Vol. 76: R. G. Swan, Algebraic K-Theory. IV, 262 pages. 1968. DM 18,– / $ 5.00

Vol. 77: P.-A. Meyer, Processus de Markov: la frontière de Martin. IV, 123 pages. 1968. DM 10,– / $ 2.80

Vol. 78: H. Herrlich, Topologische Reflexionen und Coreflexionen. XVI, 166 Seiten. 1968. DM 12,– / $ 3.30

Vol. 79: A. Grothendieck, Catégories Cofibrées Additives et Complexe Cotangent Relatif. IV, 167 pages. 1968. DM 12,– / $ 3.30

Vol. 80: Seminar on Triples and Categorical Homology Theory. Edited by B. Eckmann. IV, 398 pages. 1969. DM 20,– / $ 5.50

Vol. 81: J.-P. Eckmann et M. Guenin, Méthodes Algébriques en Mécanique Statistique. VI, 131 pages. 1969. DM 12,– / $ 3.30

Vol. 82: J. Wloka, Grundräume und verallgemeinerte Funktionen. VIII, 131 Seiten. 1969. DM 12,– / $ 3.30

Vol. 83: O. Zariski, An Introduction to the Theory of Algebraic Surfaces. IV, 100 pages. 1969. DM 8,– / $ 2.20

Vol. 84: H. Lüneburg, Transitive Erweiterungen endlicher Permutationsgruppen. IV, 119 Seiten. 1969. DM 10.– / $ 2.80

Vol. 85: P. Cartier et D. Foata, Problèmes combinatoires de commutation et réarrangements. IV, 88 pages. 1969. DM 8,– / $ 2.20

Vol. 86: Category Theory, Homology Theory and their Applications I. Edited by P. Hilton. VI, 216 pages. 1969. DM 16,– / $ 4.40

Vol. 87: M. Tierney, Categorical Constructions in Stable Homotopy Theory. IV, 65 pages. 1969. DM 6,– / $ 1.70

Vol. 88: Séminaire de Probabilités III. IV, 229 pages. 1969. DM 18,– / $ 5.00

Vol. 89: Probability and Information Theory. Edited by M. Behara, K. Krickeberg and J. Wolfowitz. IV, 256 pages. 1969. DM 18,– / $ 5.00

Vol. 90: N. P. Bhatia and O. Hajek, Local Semi-Dynamical Systems. II, 157 pages. 1969. DM 14,– / $ 3.90

Vol. 91: N. N. Janenko, Die Zwischenschrittmethode zur Lösung mehrdimensionaler Probleme der mathematischen Physik. VIII, 194 Seiten. 1969. DM 16,80 / $ 4.70

Vol. 92: Category Theory, Homology Theory and their Applications II. Edited by P. Hilton. V, 308 pages. 1969. DM 20,– / $ 5.50

Vol. 93: K. R. Parthasarathy, Multipliers on Locally Compact Groups. III, 54 pages. 1969. DM 5,60 / $ 1.60

Vol. 94: M. Machover and J. Hirschfeld, Lectures on Non-Standard Analysis. VI, 79 pages. 1969. DM 6,– / $ 1.70

Vol. 95: A. S. Troelstra, Principles of Intuitionism. II, 111 pages. 1969. DM 10,– / $ 2.80

Vol. 96: H.-B. Brinkmann und D. Puppe, Abelsche und exakte Kategorien, Korrespondenzen. V, 141 Seiten. 1969. DM 10,– / $ 2.80

Vol. 97: S. O. Chase and M. E. Sweedler, Hopf Algebras and Galois theory. II, 133 pages. 1969. DM 10,– / $ 2.80

Vol. 98: M. Heins, Hardy Classes on Riemann Surfaces. III, 106 pages. 1969. DM 10,– / $ 2.80

Vol. 99: Category Theory, Homology Theory and their Applications III. Edited by P. Hilton. IV, 489 pages. 1969. DM 24,– / $ 6.60

Vol. 100: M. Artin and B. Mazur, Etale Homotopy. II, 196 Seiten. 1969. DM 12,– / $ 3.30

Vol. 101: G. P. Szegö et G. Treccani, Semigruppi di Trasformazioni Multivoche. VI, 177 pages. 1969. DM 14,– / $ 3.90

Vol. 102: F. Stummel, Rand- und Eigenwertaufgaben in Sobolewschen Räumen. VIII, 386 Seiten. 1969. DM 20,– / $ 5.50

Vol. 103: Lectures in Modern Analysis and Applications I. Edited by C. T. Taam. VII, 162 pages. 1969. DM 12,– / $ 3.30

Vol. 104: G. H. Pimbley, Jr., Eigenfunction Branches of Nonlinear Operators and their Bifurcations. II, 128 pages. 1969. DM 10,– / $ 2.80

Vol. 105: R. Larsen, The Multiplier Problem. VII, 284 pages. 1969. DM 18,– / $ 5.00

Vol. 106: Reports of the Midwest Category Seminar III. Edited by S. Mac Lane. III, 247 pages. 1969. DM 16,– / $ 4.40

Vol. 107: A. Peyerimhoff, Lectures on Summability. III, 111 pages. 1969. DM 8,– / $ 2.20

Vol. 108: Algebraic K-Theory and its Geometric Applications. Edited by R. M.F. Moss and C. B. Thomas. IV, 86 pages. 1969. DM 6,– / $ 1.70

Vol. 109: Conference on the Numerical Solution of Differential Equations. Edited by J. Ll. Morris. VI, 275 pages. 1969. DM 18,– / $ 5.00

Vol. 110: The Many Facets of Graph Theory. Edited by G. Chartrand and S. F. Kapoor. VIII, 290 pages. 1969. DM 18,– / $ 5.00

Vol. 111: K. H. Mayer, Relationen zwischen charakteristischen Zahlen. III, 99 Seiten. 1969. DM 8,– / $ 2.20

Vol. 112: Colloquium on Methods of Optimization. Edited by N. N. Moiseev. IV, 293 pages. 1970. DM 18,– / $ 5.00

Vol. 113: R. Wille, Kongruenzklassengeometrien. III, 99 Seiten. 1970. DM 8,– / $ 2.20

Vol. 114: H. Jacquet and R. P. Langlands, Automorphic Forms on GL (2). VII, 548 pages. 1970. DM 24,– / $ 6.60

Vol. 115: K. H. Roggenkamp and V. Huber-Dyson, Lattices over Orders I. XIX, 290 pages. 1970. DM 18,– / $ 5.00

Vol. 116: Sèminaire Pierre Lelong (Analyse) Année 1969. IV, 195 pages. 1970. DM 14,– / $ 3.90

Vol. 117: Y. Meyer, Nombres de Pisot, Nombres de Salem et Analyse Harmonique. 63 pages. 1970. DM 6.– / $ 1.70

Vol. 118: Proceedings of the 15th Scandinavian Congress, Oslo 1968. Edited by K. E. Aubert and W. Ljunggren. IV, 162 pages. 1970. DM 12,– / $ 3.30

Vol. 119: M. Raynaud, Faisceaux amples sur les schémas en groupes et les espaces homogènes. III, 219 pages. 1970. DM 14,– / $ 3.90

Vol. 120: D. Siefkes, Büchi's Monadic Second Order Successor Arithmetic. XII, 130 Seiten. 1970. DM 12,– / $ 3.30

Vol. 121: H. S. Bear, Lectures on Gleason Parts. III, 47 pages. 1970. DM 6,– /$ 1.70

Vol. 122: H. Zieschang, E. Vogt und H.-D. Coldewey, Flächen und ebene diskontinuierliche Gruppen. VIII, 203 Seiten. 1970. DM 16,– / $ 4.40

Vol. 123: A. V. Jategaonkar, Left Principal Ideal Rings. VI, 145 pages. 1970. DM 12,– / $ 3.30

Vol. 124: Séminare de Probabilités IV. Edited by P. A. Meyer. IV, 282 pages. 1970. DM 20,– / $ 5.50

Vol. 125: Symposium on Automatic Demonstration. V, 310 pages. 1970. DM 20,– / $ 5.50

Vol. 126: P. Schapira, Théorie des Hyperfonctions. XI, 157 pages. 1970. DM 14,– / $ 3.90

Vol. 127: I. Stewart, Lie Algebras. IV, 97 pages. 1970. DM 10,– / $ 2.80

Vol. 128: M. Takesaki, Tomita's Theory of Modular Hilbert Algebras and its Applications. II, 123 pages. 1970. DM 10,– / $ 2.80

Vol. 129: K. H. Hofmann, The Duality of Compact Semigroups and C*- Bigebras. XII, 142 pages. 1970. DM 14,– / $ 3.90

Vol. 130: F. Lorenz, Quadratische Formen über Körpern. II, 77 Seiten. 1970. DM 8,– / $ 2.20

Vol. 131: A Borel et al., Seminar on Algebraic Groups and Related Finite Groups. VII, 321 pages. 1970. DM 22,– / $ 6.10

Vol. 132: Symposium on Optimization. III, 348 pages. 1970. DM 22,– / $ 6.10

Vol. 133: F. Topsøe, Topology and Measure. XIV, 79 pages. 1970. DM 8,– / $ 2.20

Vol. 134: L. Smith, Lectures on the Eilenberg-Moore Spectral Sequence. VII, 142 pages. 1970. DM 14,– / $ 3.90

Vol. 135: W. Stoll, Value Distribution of Holomorphic Maps into Compact Complex Manifolds. II, 267 pages. 1970. DM 18,– / $ 5.00

Vol. 136: M. Karoubi et al., Séminaire Heidelberg-Saarbrücken-Strasbuorg sur la K-Théorie. IV, 264 pages. 1970. DM 18,– / $ 5.00

Vol. 137: Reports of the Midwest Category Seminar IV. Edited by S. MacLane. III, 139 pages. 1970. DM 12,– / $ 3.30

Vol. 138: D. Foata et M. Schützenberger, Théorie Géométrique des Polynômes Eulériens. V, 94 pages. 1970. DM 10,– / $ 2.80

Vol. 139: A. Badrikian, Séminaire sur les Fonctions Aléatoires Linéaires et les Mesures Cylindriques. VII, 221 pages. 1970. DM 18,– / $ 5.00

Vol. 140: Lectures in Modern Analysis and Applications II. Edited by C. T. Taam. VI, 119 pages. 1970. DM 10,– / $ 2.80